An Armenian Family Reunion

An Armenian Family Reunion

BY
Mitchell Kalpakgian

THE NEUMANN PRESS

www.neumannpress.com

ISBN 1-930873-88-3

PRINTED, BOUND AND PUBLISHED BY THE NEUMANN PRESS
LONG PRAIRIE, MINNESOTA, UNITED STATES OF AMERICA

DEDICATION

To the Armenian martyrs who died for their Christian faith and passed on to the Armenian people and eventually to my family and to me the good news about God's inestimable love for every human being as a precious gift from Heaven.

To my parents Khatchig and Meline (Manouelian) Kalpakgian who loved and cared for me, my brother Aris, and my sister Nancy with all their heart and soul, who made us the center of their life, and who made every sacrifice for our happiness.

To my beloved family members on both sides of our family who enriched my life with mirth, laughter, fun, affection, and kindness from the abundance of their generous hearts and their bountiful hospitality—my grandmother Elise Manouelian and my aunt Arousiag Manouelian; my aunts and uncles Hagop and Araxi Balian and David and Virginia Kalpakgian; my cousins Laura (Balian) Harotian, Blanche (Balian) Berberian, Rose (Balian) Manoogian, Harry Kalpakgian Edward Kalpakgian, Olga Kalpakgian, and Gregory Kalpakgian; and to "Grandpa" Eli Hovagimian.

To my wife Joyce (Narsasian) Kalpakgian and our five children—Gregory, Aram, Mark, Tanya, and Peter—for the riches of love and the fullness of joy they have provided so that "my cup runneth over."

To my wife's family, the Narsasians and Ashodians, for their pure hearts of gold that never stop giving.

ACKNOWLEDGMENTS

A Special Thank You to

MICHAEL MANOOGIAN, *Photography*

GREGORY APRAHAMIAN, *Illustrations*

Preface

When I was a young man in my twenties pursuing graduate degrees in English and preparing for a career in teaching, my father—a survivor of the Turkish genocide of the Armenians in 1915— urged me, "Mitch, you should write my story!" About forty years later in my sixties, I heard that voice again, even though my father had been deceased for twenty years. I was sitting upstairs on the couch in the den wondering how I should spend the leisure of my summer when the idea of this book came to me by way of inspiration from the Holy Spirit. Those words kept resonating in my mind, "Mitch, you should write my story." Of course I, of all people, the educator and English major in the family, should write Khatchig Kalpakgian's story, and I should write it before it was too late! But, the Holy Spirit was whispering, I should also write all those other unforgettable, delightful, illuminating stories which I remember today as if they happened just yesterday—stories which were told to me by other family members or stories I heard in conversations or stories I experienced first-hand. Like proverbs and folk tales, family stories and conversations embody sources of perennial wisdom to be passed down from one generation to another.

What better way of concluding my life's destiny and completing the final chapters of the seven ages of man than by recalling, reliving, and savoring the fullness of a person's human experience from birth to old age. In these pages appear the colorful, inimitable, unrepeatable creations of human beings that form the radical individuality and variety of human nature, described by Gerard Manley Hopkins in "Comments on the Spiritual Exercises of St. Ignatius Loyola" as "being more highly pitched and distinctive than anything in the world." G. K. Chesterton is absolutely right: "the supreme adventure is being born," and being born is "the wildest of adventures." Once we are born and introduced to family life, we are surprised again because "The real family is something as wild and elemental as a cabbage." Armenian families especially fit this description.

When Shakespeare's Jaques lamented that life's "strange eventful history" is dull repetition and no more than "a stage" in which every scene and act from birth to death is a tiresome continuation of melancholic experiences from "the mewling and puking" infant and "whining school-boy" to the old man in "second childishness and mere oblivion," he ignored the wildness of the family, and of course he did not know any Armenians. Growing up in an extended Armenian family of old-world immigrants, I testify that Chesterton had to be talking about my relatives when he wrote,

> Our father and mother do lie in wait for us and leap out on us, like brigands from a bush. Our uncle is a surprise. Our aunt is, in the beautiful common expression, a bolt from the blue. When we step into the family, by the act of being born, we do step into a world which is incalculable, into a world which has its own strange laws, into a world which could do without us, into a world that we have not made. In other words, when we step into the family we step into a fairy-tale.

In these stories appear the "wild" people who loved me the most, taught me the most, delighted me the most, enriched me the most, and surprised me the most. Thank God for wild Armenians, wild families, and for the gift of life as the wildest of adventures.

Contents

CHAPTER ONE

The Family Reunion

The Bedrosian family finally organized their first family reunion. The three brothers and two sisters, having grown up in Massachusetts, had married or taken jobs in various parts of the country. After the deaths of their parents in the 1980's—their parents were immigrants who had escaped the horrific Turkish genocide of the Armenians perpetrated during World War I—the adult children had no natural gathering place such as the family home where everyone came during Christmas or during summer vacations.

The oldest son Stepan (Armenian for Stephen) felt it incumbent upon him to initiate some event of this kind. He and his brothers and sisters and all their children were beginning to lose contact and drift into their own worlds of work and pleasure, visiting each other periodically but not on a regular or annual basis. It was the Christmas celebration, and the Bedrosians were not able to gather as one large extended family in one place to enjoy the holy season or to taste the fullness of joy that accompanies the birth of Christ.

Nubar and Elise Bedrosian had left to their children a modest inheritance of $20,000 with the stipulation that each of the grandchildren receive a $1,000 graduation gift after completing high school. The money had been invested in a certificate of deposit that matured every two years. Now that all the grandchildren had graduated, a balance of $12,000 remained. Rather than divide the money evenly among the five children and close the account, Stepan had proposed using some of the money for a family reunion, giving each family a stipend of $1,000 to use for transportation to attend this gala family event. He knew that his parents would have naturally approved of this project and that family solidarity was a deeply ingrained Armenian trait. How often had he as the oldest son heard these words as a child: "Be sure to take care of your younger brothers at the park and always hold their hands when you cross the street!" Upon returning home from college Stepan and his brothers and sisters were of course expected to visit their grandparents and aunts and uncles as a token of respect or honor. So Stepan felt strongly that his parents would rejoice in Heaven to know of the Bedrosian reunion. No doubt they had inspired the idea in the first place and were urging him to organize the event.

His youngest sister Anahid liked the idea instantly and volunteered to organize it if everyone were willing to come. Living near Lake Okoboji in western Iowa, a central meeting place for everyone since one brother lived in California and another one in Kansas, Anahid's practical intelligence and instant common sense came into play. "I know just the place," she assured her oldest brother. "On West Okoboji Lake where our family has vacationed often, there are several cottages arranged in a big circle right on the water that would be ideal," she insisted. She pictured everything in her mind in a flash. Each family would have its own cottage; the children of high school and college ages would enjoy boundless pleasure in the nearby recreation room with ping-pong, billiards, and fuss ball, on the baseball field, soccer field, and tennis courts close at hand, and at the beach with available canoes and rowboats for the older children. The adults could savor each other's company throughout the day and especially during the evenings, hearing of the latest events in each other's lives and renewing their friendships with one another. In Anahid's opinion Stepan had a great idea. "Mom and Dad would have loved this," Anahid kept telling herself. In each of her conversations with her brothers and sisters, she heard herself repeating, "They would have wanted us to spend the money for occasions just like this one!" Everyone agreed. It dawned on

Anahid that this was a clear example of the Christian teaching about the communion of saints—the oneness between the living and the dead who continue to play a vital role in each other's lives despite their physical separation.

Because this was the first reunion since the death of the parents eight years ago and since the clan missed each other as a larger extended family—communicating only at Christmas and through occasional telephone calls— the response was surprisingly positive. With the bonus of $1,000 as an incentive to ease the financial burden, with the thought of a week's vacation in the good company of family members, and with the knowledge that all the children would have a fun-loving time and know their cousins as good friends, the Bedrosian clan committed themselves to a two-week vacation at West Okoboji Lake. The first formal Bedrosian family reunion was proposed and ratified—at least by the adults. The reactions of the cousins to their Uncle Stepan's novel proposal, however, were mixed and less than enthusiastic, but they soon changed their minds.

As the winter and spring months passed and summer approached, everyone gave more thought to the idea of the reunion. Michael, the second oldest in the family, mentioned to Anahid that the evenings would be a perfect time to reminisce and recall favorite stories, fond memories, and family history. "Let's agree that no one will bring a TV and that none of the teenage children will bring audiotapes or compact discs for music. Tell everyone they can bring their favorite games, cards, musical instruments, and sports equipment but no TV viewing, no videos, and no loud music!" Anahid was not too certain about the popularity of this proposal but promised to mention it to the other members of the family. Of course there was some protesting, especially on the part of some of the college-age members that the evenings might become boring and repetitious without musical entertainment, but all the parents, on the whole, favored the idea—only a few bemoaning missing their favorite sports teams in action or their news channels. "It's only two weeks! You'll live!" were the compelling arguments that settled the issue.

Michael had given serious thought to the storytelling

idea, recalling what his eighteen-year-old son had told him one evening when Michael and his wife Anna had hosted a dinner party with friends that just naturally led to lively conversations on politics, religion, the state of the culture, and the world of difference between the parents' childhood and the early growing years of their own children.

"Dad," his son Mark commented, "my friends and I learn so much when we hear the adults talk about all those subjects you and your friends discuss. One evening of listening to your stories and discussions is worth three months of sitting in a classroom and never hearing informed, intelligent conversation by people who read and think and have clear moral views. I love it, and then at school on Monday during lunch we talk about the things I heard discussed at our house. I tell my friends that Margaret Sanger was a racist and explain eugenics to them—an idea that never appeared in the textbook or in class. I told them about Margaret Sanger's desire to create 'a race of thoroughbreds' and her desire to eliminate 'unfit' people from the human race—Slavic people, southeastern Europeans, Jews, and Blacks. You never hear those views in school or read them in any of the textbooks. In school they make a hero of Margaret Sanger—proclaiming her as some great intellectual woman leader because the textbook mentions her name and shows her picture—but no teacher or student knows the facts and the story as I heard it at home during the party. Nobody connects Margaret Sanger the racist with Margaret Sanger the founder of Planned Parenthood."

Michael took that statement to heart. The home was a school. Sitting at the table and talking about things in general is the basis of culture. When young people witness the passions and convictions of the people they love and respect speak from their life's experience and knowledge and then share and compare their knowledge in the exchange of honest conversation, the minds and hearts of the young come alive. Thinking becomes exciting. Reading becomes an energizing activity. The older generation is transmitting wisdom to the younger generation. "Old birds are teaching young birds how to fly," as C. S. Lewis had remarked in THE ABOLITION OF MAN, one of Michael's favorite books.

"What a wonderful opportunity for all of us to do that as an extended family!" Michael had thought. So a month before the July reunion Michael had called his brothers and sisters and proposed that each night someone from each family—father, mother, or child—tell a story. "We can each recall our favorite tales about Mom and Dad and tell the children what it was like to be first generation Armenians living in two worlds: the Armenian culture in our homes and the American way we learned in schools and in the neighborhood. We can tell them about how we husbands and wives met—funny, moving stories with strange coincidences. We all have a repertory we can draw from. They can be serious stories, funny anecdotes, love stories, miraculous tales, folk tales, or proverbs we heard from the relatives, and of course the children should all know how Dad narrowly escaped death at the hands of the Turks. That should be the first story, and let Stepan tell that one. Over the years I remember him drawing out from Dad the various episodes in his life. He knows almost all the important details about Dad's escape. The children will be moved and inspired and thank God profoundly for the gift of life they enjoy because of the hand of Divine Providence in their grandfather's life. This is their heritage, and they all need to hear this. In this age especially when young people refer to themselves as Generation X, they need a heritage, a tradition, a family history so that they realize a torch has been handed down to them and that they too must preserve and transmit the best of the past to another generation."

"That's fine," Anahid replied. "When I send everyone the letter with all the details, directions, and final plans, I'll mention the storytelling idea so that each family will prepare something. Actually, I think we should record these stories and then make duplicate audiotapes for everyone to have and replay. I'll call Melanie and tell her to bring a recorder. Armen works in the communications business and can bring the right equipment from work. This is good. Everyone is offering ideas, Stepan the idea of the reunion, I the location of Lake Okoboji, you, Michael, the oral history of the family. I'm going to check with Melanie and Tomas and see if they have any other thoughts about what to do or what to bring before we finalize the plans. I know Tomas loves to organize athletic events and will no doubt be planning soccer games, baseball games, frisbee, fishing contests, and all kinds of competition. With his background as a camp director and soccer coach, he'll keep everyone active and occupied. Melanie is such a good cook and a great lover of potluck dinners. I know she will want to plan the meals and organize the kitchen work into teams and divisions of labor. She's a genius at organization and will assign jobs and oversee everything so that no one person is overburdened or a slave in the kitchen. Everyone from young to old will help. That's a great way to know one another and to feel a sense of belonging to something larger than one's self. On this vacation the extended family will replace the nuclear family."

Anahid's telephone calls to her brother and sister reassured her that everyone from the youngest to the oldest in their families was excited about this vacation. Of course Tomas wanted to be the recreation director for morning activities, and naturally Melanie wanted to do all the shopping, planning, and cooking of the evening meals. Her daughter Mariam would bring her guitar and song music for part of each evening's pleasure.

"Why haven't we thought of this before?" Melanie uttered in their telephone conversation. "That's the problem with mobility. We all move because of jobs and marriages, but we imagine we will keep up our correspondence and visit on holidays and summers, but it's only a matter of time before the weariness and expense of traveling—especially with young children— soon discourage us. Instead of seeing each other once or twice a year, we are lucky if it's once in four years. Instead of living as an extended family or clan, we have nuclear families. The children hardly get to know their aunts and uncles and cousins. Oh, yes, we all live comfortable lives and own good homes, but we work too much, become too busy, and don't think of anyone else except our immediate family. I think our own lives in Milford, Massachusetts, where our grandparents and uncles and aunts were just a few miles away, offered a richer life. You came to really know your relatives and have affection for them. Because of the constant contact you learned the story of their lives and came to appreciate their good hearts and learned to laugh at their eccentric quirks."

"That's true," Anahid replied. "I can't disagree with you. In our mobility we gain something, but we also lose something. Maybe what we lose is of far more value than what we gain. We lose the family bonds, we can't enjoy the holidays together, we can't be of help to each other when a baby arrives or when we need a babysitter, and we lose our sense of cultural identity. In Iowa and the Midwest in general virtually no one recognizes your Armenian name, hardly knows anything about the Turkish genocide of the Armenians, or is even curious about your ethnic background. I know, we all have great friends and human nature is the same everywhere, but I just miss the closeness we used to feel and the larger network of relatives that used to surround us in our childhood."

"I know exactly what you mean," Melanie answered. "The great thing about our growing up was that what you heard from Mom and Dad, you also heard from auntie and uncle and from Grandma and Grandpa. There was no moral confusion about right and wrong, about what it meant to be a woman or what it meant to be a man, about the purpose of life being to marry and raise families, about the reality of God. Today the great danger for children is that there is no such universal moral consensus. What children learn in the home, for example, is contradicted in the schools in their so-called health programs and contradicted in movies and television. I can't believe the way they are defining 'family' these days as any kind of arrangement between all sorts of people—married or unmarried. Growing up was so much easier for us than it is for our own children. Everybody knew what 'normal,' 'natural,' and 'moral' meant.

Many thoughts came to Anahid. "Do you know what I most remember about Mom and Dad's old-world wisdom? I overheard this conversation several times at the dinner table as Dad was drinking his coffee and Mom was finishing the cleaning of the kitchen. They would both say, 'Life is so simple. God's plan is so clear.' They meant that happiness comes in giving to one another—husbands and wives giving to one another, the parents loving the children, the children helping each other, each family bringing friendship and charity to other families. They especially liked the way Father Hagopian used to explain this great circle of love: husbands and wives are to be 'sources of grace' to each other and to their children; the children, in turn, are to be sources of grace and goodness to their parents and to their brothers and sisters; and the entire family is to be a source of grace and blessing to other families. How simple and true that is! I'll never forget those sayings. It all makes such perfect sense."

These reflections sparked similar memories for Melanie. She continued, "I especially remembered how Mom explained the simplicity of life and the clarity of God's moral law by always referring to the Ten Commandments. She truly followed all of them. Also I remember her saying that so many social problems could be eliminated 'if mothers just stayed at home and took care of their children.' She was adamant about this. In fact, I remember that when she was asked to do babysitting for some families, she was firm about saying no because she did not want to be party to mothers leaving their children to go to work. Even though she hated the idea of babysitting other women's children when she knew these mothers really did not absolutely have to work, she felt sorry for the children and did it on a short-term basis."

Anahid also remembered overhearing some of those conversations as Dad lingered over his coffee at the dinner table. She added, "When they would discuss the simplicity of life and the self-evident design of God's purposes, he would frequently say that God made man and woman fertile for a long period of time. Why? Because He intended men and women to have large families. He could not figure out why other people could not see that basic truth. He could not imagine men in their prime years choosing to have vasectomies or women deciding to have tubal ligations after two children. 'Be fruitful and multiply.' How clear, simple, and sensible!"

"That's what I loved the most about them," replied Melanie. "Their simplicity! They were not complicated people.

They worked hard. They told the truth. They loved their children. They were devoted to their extended families. They had such a strong sense of duty. They had such a clear moral sense. They recognized that happy families are nourished by good food, fun, laughter, and hospitality—simple things! They had this wonderful grasp of the difference between the essential and the non-essential. I know we did not have many things, either many clothes or many toys or any luxuries. But we knew that there was nothing that Mom and Dad would not do for us. If it was good and right for us, they would have made every sacrifice of time, money, or energy. Do you remember the words of Michael Arlen in PASSAGE to ARARAT? They are so true: "There is nothing an Armenian father will not do for his children."

"Wow! This is turning into quite a conversation. I didn't realize how long we have been talking," Anahid said. "We can certainly continue discussions like this one at the reunion. If this is a preview, what a wonderful event this is going to be! I'm so glad we're finally doing something like this. The children will realize that they are a part of something larger than themselves, that they are not alone in the world but surrounded by a family of young and old, that they are the beneficiaries of a noble tradition, that so much has been given to them for them to pass on to others. Well, we all have something out of the ordinary to look forward to this summer. Let's keep in touch. If you have other thoughts or ideas about the reunion, just call, alright? "

CHAPTER TWO

The Quixotic, Old-World Bedrosians

Everyone arrived at West Okoboji Lake in the best of spirits for a two-week vacation in July. Tomas's family had flown from Sacramento to Sioux City and then rented a car. Melanie's family from New Jersey also arrived by plane and was greeted by Anahid and her husband Dickran at the airport. Stepan and his clan had driven from Ann Arbor, Michigan, and Michael with his wife and children had traveled by car from Lawrence, Kansas. It surprised everyone on the day of arrival that all of these travel plans could be coordinated. The family reunion was not just a sentiment or a theory. A remote idea had crystallized; the vague had become clear. Stepan remembered the title of Richard Weaver's book which he had read in college: "Ideas have consequences." He also remembered a passage he cherished from Hannah Arendt's THE HUMAN CONDITION: to act is to begin, to initiate, to take the first step, to cause movement. Once a process is begun, it carries its own momentum, and others join and participate, and before long the idea assumes a life of its own.

As Stepan sees all the happy faces, handshakes, and hugs during arrivals of the relatives, he rejoices in the thought that this dream has become reality. He did not merely think about a family reunion but felt a strong conviction. The idea did not go away but kept resurfacing. It not only made sense as a practical measure for the family members to renew their relationships but also created an occasion for pure fun and true leisure. He became more and more excited and enthusiastic every time he thought about the possibility. He was amazed and delighted at the instant cooperation and help he received from the other members of the family. The whole project simply needed a leader—not someone to do all the planning or all the work or all the organizing but simply someone to demonstrate leadership and propose the idea with seriousness and sincerity.

It reminded Stepan of his wife Lori's spontaneous pot-luck dinners. A widower, he missed his wife profoundly and thought of how much she would have relished this occasion. She had died of breast cancer four years ago, and the void in his life was enormous. Nevertheless, he felt as if she were present in motivating him to plan this vacation and offering ideas. Carried away by her friendliness and delighting in the company and conversation of old friends or new acquaintances after church, Lori would invite them to the house for "coffee." However, it wasn't exactly coffee that was served. Yes, the coffee was brewing, but at the same time the choreg (Armenian sweet bread) was being defrosted and heated, and the butter, jam, honey, and cheese were spreading on the kitchen table. One of the invited couples would decide to buy some scones at a nearby bakery, and another couple remembered that they had some cornbread at home they wanted to share, while another couple stopped to buy some grapes, cherries, and watermelon from a fruit stand. What a great time everyone would have! The happy occasion was not formally organized but happened serendipitously because his wife followed her heart and took the first step. Everyone is longing for such happenings, but so many people just wait for others to make the invitation. Stepan had learned both from his wife and his parents how to let the Holy Spirit direct him; he recognized these inspirations and came to discern their particular savor.

How fondly he remembered Nubar and Elise Bedrosian's style of old-world hospitality. They rarely made formal invitations for dinner or carefully organized dinner parties. They simply told friends and relatives to "stop over some time." They always felt honored to have visitors and welcomed them heartily.

During their visit his parents would plead, "Oh, please, please stay for dinner. Everything is already made. You can eat and go if you are busy, but please have dinner with us." How could anyone disappoint such sincerity? The smells from the kitchen and the warm friendliness of course made the invitation irresistible. Stepan remembered what a great time everyone had. His mother and father were so animated, so full of conversation, reminiscence, anecdote, proverbs, and laughter during these occasions. He loved seeing this social side of his parents because it revealed to them the depths of their goodness and kindness. Nubar and Elise Bedrosian were to Stepan the originals for Hawthorne's story about Baucis and Philemon. Yes, their boundless hearts were "miraculous pitchers" that could not be depleted. The more milk the guests drank at the table of Baucis and Philemon, the sooner the pitcher was mysteriously filled again. They knew how to follow their hearts and let themselves be carried away by charity and good will. Having learned from his parents, Stepan too was unafraid to take these first steps and initiate something good. He rejoiced to see so many happy faces and smiles arriving for the reunion. Somehow he knew he was continuing a great tradition.

Everyone's joy was palpable. Despite the weariness of traveling, everyone looked relaxed and in a festive mood. Stepan liked hearing all the greetings: "So good to see you!" "It's been too long! It's about time for us to get together!" "Melanie, your children are so beautiful!" "Siran, you look wonderful!" "Michael, you look so distinguished with your gray hair. You need to run for political office." Stepan also noticed the instant compatibility among the cousins. Despite growing up in different parts of the country and being subject to various American cultural influences, it was obvious to him that the *primary* educational influence upon these children was the formation they received from their parents in their Armenian homes. The children all looked normal—no men with long, disheveled hair or ear-rings or dyed hair, no women with pierced bodies or nose rings.

The morning and early afternoon were spent unloading vehicles, unpacking suitcases, and making beds. Everyone was carrying suitcases for the newly arrived families, and everyone was congregating by their cabins. It was not long before the cousins began joining each other and playing. The appearance of a soccer ball, a frisbee, and baseball gloves soon occupied some of the cousins. The separation of time and distance somehow did not make a great difference for the young. Play is a universal language, and the cousins sensed their natural bonds with one another. They had all been raised by at least one of the Bedrosians, and so the Bedrosian spirit, heart, and affability was evident in their manner toward one another. They had heard over and over again that their cousins were not just ordinary friends but close family members with whom they shared a common history and background. Without expressing it in words, the cousins felt a special affection for one another. Over the years they relished comparing stories about their parents, whom they quickly categorized as in a class by themselves. The phrase that made them roar was a line from HAMLET that Stepan's son Haig encountered in an English class: his father was a little bit "north-north west" as he put it. All the Bedrosians had a touch of Don Quixote's madness according to their children. Soon that afternoon as the children gathered by the lake to enjoy the sun and water, the teen-age children quickly found a topic of general interest.

The teen-age cousins especially liked to compare notes on the strangeness or eccentricity of their parents. "No, Dad, you are not normal like the other fathers of my friends at home," Michael's oldest daughter Talene would say teasingly. "We don't ever watch television! You never even give permission for us to go to the movies unless the film is G-rated. The only films that are G-rated are the Walt Disney ones. Is that what we're supposed to see? Why do you worry so much? My friends' parents never ask them so many questions about movies!" Of course the other cousins all had their versions of similar zany stories.

"My mother won't buy anything in the stores that has a single preservative in it," Anahid's daughter Lucy protested. "Everything has to be organic and whole wheat, and the labels can't have nitrites or BHA or BHT on them. None of my friends ever eat our food when they are at the house! No one likes whole wheat spaghetti or cookies that have honey in them instead of sugar. See, our parents are strange, aren't they?"

The joking would continue. Melanie's son Vahan could hardly wait to tell his howler. "Do you know what we had to do before our mother agreed to buy a VCR so we could watch some good movies at home?" All four of us had to read ten books, all of them approved by Mom or Dad. They were to pick out half the books, and we could pick out the other half. Isn't that stupid? Dad even made me as the oldest son write out a contract, and then all of us had to sign it. They would buy the video cassette recorder only when all three of us had completed our reading. So naturally we kept asking each other, 'What book are you on?' Then we would prod each other: 'Did you do your reading today? What page are you on?' It was like a big project with all the fast, avid readers always pestering the slower, less eager ones. It's amazing. How we all hated this and thought it the craziest idea. What other family do you know that makes its children sign a contract and read books to get points or credits for a VCR? Unreal! I will admit that it was good for us, and we're not sorry for reading some of the classics like LITTLE MEN, THE PRINCESS AND THE GOBLIN, and THE WIND IN THE WILLOWS. And now we laugh about it, but only in the Bedrosian family would such 'kookiness' rule the day."

"They are originals, that's for sure," added Michael's son Aram. "My father loves to tell the story about Grandpa Nubar when Jehovah's Witnesses came to the house to win converts to their religion. Of course Grandpa barely understood English, let alone a discussion about the finer points of religion. My father always mentions Grandpa puffing on his cigar and listening intently, never saying a word. The visitor had spoken at length for five or ten minutes, assuming that Grandpa was seriously interested. When the Jehovah's Witness had finished speaking and had offered Grandpa a copy of their publication, he looked dumbfounded when Grandpa finally spoke in his gruff, loud voice: 'Naw, naw, we don't want any! We already got our own God!' That ended the discussion for sure."

"How about the other stories about Grandpa? Do you know the ones about his locksmithing adventures?" Melanie's daughter Tamar asked. "Mom bursts with laughter every time she tells this one. Grandpa had received a call to change some locks in an older woman's home a few miles out of town. It must have been in the winter because when he knocked on the door, the lady told him to come and take off his rubbers. 'No, M'am, I ain't taking off any rubbers,' he said peevishly as he waited at the entrance. 'Do you want the locks fixed or not?' 'Well, no, not if you're going walking all over my house with your wet and dirty rubbers!' she argued. He didn't say a word, but with his toolbox in his hand just turned around and started walking back to his car. 'Come here, come here!' she yelled. 'For goodness' sake just come in and fix my locks. I've never met anyone like you before!' 'Do you want me to come in or not?' he retaliated. 'Yes, come and do your job. I'm not going to say another word.' That's the story. Grandpa, I guess, was not going to humor everyone's whims. You had to take him or leave him. He would not be made a fool or treated like a flunkey. He thought that wiping his rubbers on the mat was adequate and that anything beyond that expectation was insulting. Uncle Stepan was there as Grandpa's helper and remembers every detail. Ask him."

"Speaking about insults," Tomas's son Peter interjected, "my Dad remembers the time Dr. Berry came into Grandpa's shop to pick up a lock that needed repair and needed to be fitted for a key. When Dr.Berry , known in town as a wealthy physician, came to get the key, Grandpa handed it to him with a skeleton key in the keyhole. 'How much?' the doctor asked. 'Five dollars,' Grandpa said matter-of-factly. 'What! Five dollars! For one key! You have to be kidding! That is robbery! I'm not giving you five dollars to make a d--- skeleton key for an old lock! You're crazy!' Guess what Grandpa did? He took the key out of the lock, kept the key in his hand, returned the lock to Dr. Berry, and yelled in return, 'Take your key and get the h - - - out of here! Don't ever come back. I don't want to see your face again!' My father was there and in shock. He could not believe the doctor had spoken so insultingly and accused Grandpa of cheating and overcharging. Everyone paid the standard $5.00 to have a key fitted for a lock. For a moment Dad wasn't sure how this argument would turn. He thought maybe the doctor would accept the price or maybe Grandpa would lower the price or maybe they would compromise. When the doctor grabbed his lock and walked away in a huff, Dad (who was only about 17 at the time) said to Grandpa, 'Dad, that was great! That was terrific! That is exactly the treatment Dr. Berry deserved. He thought that just because he was a doctor and you were a locksmith that he could bully you and get his way.' Dad said that that was one of the greatest moral lessons he ever learned: if you are right, you don't compromise your principles, and you don't let yourself be bullied or intimidated by anyone."

"There's one more Grandpa Nubar story that's hilarious," Anahid's son Levon continued. "Have you heard the witch story? Grandpa had done work for a woman in Medway, about ten miles away from Milford, but when she called him to do additional work, he refused to go. 'Dad, why aren't you going? I'll watch the store. Business is slow, and this will be a good day's work for you,' Uncle Stepan had told him. Here is Grandpa's answer. You won't believe this, but he actually said it and believed it: 'Not at that woman's house. I ain't ever going there again.' Uncle was puzzled and kept asking, 'Why, Dad? What's the problem? She didn't pay you? She asked you to take off your rubbers?' This is what Grandpa said: 'That woman is a witch. Can't you tell by her eyes? I'm never stepping into that house again or going near her.' Someone would think we are imagining or making up all these stories, but our fathers and mothers swear by them."

The cousins were bursting in laughter. The tales all sounded like classic Bedrosian humor. The older children saw traces of their grandparents in their parents. What distinctive, colorful personalities! They were all unrepeatable creations. There was no one like them or who even remotely resembled them, and that was one of the things that made them all so lovable: they were not afraid to be themselves. You never knew what they were thinking or what they would say. They were never indecisive, they were never vague about what is right or what is wrong, they held deep convictions and strong opinions, and they always gave advice that sounded infallible. The Bedrosians never struggled with the purpose or meaning of life; they would be the last to agonize with Hamlet, "To be or not to be." To marry, to found homes, to raise children, to be faithful in marriage, to pass on the wisdom of the past, and to love their Christian faith were the clear designs of God's plan, and happiness came from following them. For all their eccentricities the Bedrosian elders nevertheless impressed their children with their astounding common sense, great prudence, remarkable wisdom, and warm humanity.

CHAPTER THREE

The Harvest of Life

Everyone was soon feeling right at home. Some of the cousins had played soccer in the early afternoon, enjoyed their lunch, and were swimming in the lake by late afternoon. At a nearby picnic table another group of the cousins were conversing about their schools, their college majors, and their summer jobs, obviously enjoying each other's company and friendship. A few were playing tennis or canoeing. Looking at such scenes, the Bedrosian parents and their spouses were enjoying the harvest of their lives, the fruitfulness of love that happy families produce. As they were gathered in their folding chairs at the beach, Anahid remarked, "Do you know what this afternoon reminds me of? I can't help but think of the ending of Louisa May Alcott's LITTLE WOMEN. Maybe some of you saw the movie. You've read that book, Melanie, and Michael, you teach it in your children's literature course at Kansas, don't you? Do you remember the final chapter called "Harvesttime"? It's Mrs. March's sixtieth birthday. All of the married sisters with their husbands and children are gathered to honor their mother during this special celebration of the apple-picking season. Yes, it's the harvest of the fall, the apple-picking season in all its abundance. But there's also a harvest of life, the harvest of the family, which can also be a cornucopia."

"Don't you love what the March sisters say to their mother

at her birthday?" Melanie interrupted. "Seeing the happiness of all three generations in this time of the fall harvest, Jo March bursts out, 'I do think that families are the most beautiful things in the whole world.' Meg says to her mother that because she has a modest home, a husband, and some dear children, she is 'the happiest woman in the world.' Then Amy says that she agrees with Meg: 'Thank God, I'm a happy woman,' explaining that she also is blessed with a loving husband and a beautiful daughter. But the final line is the most beautiful of all, Mrs. March turning to her daughters and rejoicing in their happiness as married women and witnessing the joy of her grandchildren. She concludes the novel with these most unforgettable lines: 'Oh, my girls, however long you may live, I never can wish you any greater happiness than this.' How often today do we hear a message like this? All we hear about is the inconveniences, burdens, and conflicts that go with raising children. I was looking at one of the books in the high school health curriculum, and there was a statement in it like, "From birth to age twenty-two it costs an average of $75,000 to raise a child." Some ridiculous number like that—as if parents think of children in terms of dollars or cents!"

"That reminds me of one of Planned Parenthood's recent ads," Michael remembered. "It goes something like, 'Children are noisy, smelly, and expensive.' Of course those who write those ads and have those thoughts were born quiet, clean-smelling, and cheap to raise. What nonsense! Acting with two sets of standards, one for the living and one for the unborn. I remember one time I was teaching C. S. Lewis's THE ABOLITION OF MAN. I asked the students why different cultures from the ancient Chinese to the Arabic to the Old Norse recognized the evil of adultery, dishonesty, and theft. They saw clearly that these acts were absolutely evil because of the injury involved; they were inherently wrong, the students said, because no one wanted to be cheated in marriage, deceived, or robbed; therefore, one should not do to others what one does not want done to him—simple moral common sense, the golden rule. So I said to the students, 'Do you see why abortion is as wrong as adultery, dishonesty, and theft? Would *you* want to be aborted? Would *you* want to be dismembered, mutilated, burned, or poisoned? After I asked this question, I saw some angry, hostile looks, and one of the women raised her hand and said, 'But you don't have any right to tell us abortion is wrong. That is just your opinion and your religious view.' Our culture has done an unbelievable job of propagandizing the idea that children are the enemies of personal happiness and self-fulfillment."

"By the way," Tomas's wife Siran interjected, "speaking of LITTLE WOMEN, did you see the recent Hollywood version of the book? It appeared in the mid 90's. They left out completely the final episode in the novel, the chapter called 'Harvesttime' when the family reunion occurs and all the March sisters comment on the beauty of families and the happiness that goes with being mothers. Instead they ended the movie with the romances climaxing in marriages, but no presentation of the fruitfulness of families and the abundance of children and grandchildren. A very telling omission! It just wouldn't be politically correct to offend the feminists for whom motherhood is slavery and menial servitude. It simply is not *a la mode* to present large happy families as the norm."

Tomas himself added, "I feel so marginalized at the college where I coach. They recently gave an honorary degree to a liberal Democratic senator who votes in favor of partial-birth abortion—killing nine-month old babies in the womb as they are being born. The policies in colleges these days make no sense at all—neither educational sense, moral sense, nor common sense. Dormitories become brothels, the nurses dispense free contraceptives presumably 'to prevent AIDS,' some faculty openly cohabit, tolerance is the only virtue, and multiculturalism and diversity (in other words, anything is allowed) are the only religion. "I've needed a good conversation like this for a long time. It's great to know that others are thinking the same thoughts because I often feel that I'm a voice in the wilderness surrounded by so much nonsense and that I'm the only one who keeps arguing that 2+2=4.

"I can't even read newspapers any more," Tomas continued. "I don't trust NBC or CBS news programs. I don't trust school administrators or educators. Everywhere—in all the major institutions—all I see is the anti-life, anti-child, anti-family mentality. Schools push contraception, doctors are always asking you—right after the birth of a child—what kind of contraception you are going to use, or they inquire if you desire a tubal ligation. About $60 million of our tax dollars go toward promoting 'family planning' in other countries. These nations need food and medicine, but instead they get pills, contraception, and sterilization. When we were discussing GULLIVER'S TRAVELS many years ago in one of my college classes, I remember the professor saying 'the world always has been and always will be essentially mad.' What a statement! I wonder what Swift would be writing if he lived at the end of the twentieth century. I'm glad to escape the mad world of academe and return to the sane world of family.

"I can guess what Swift would satirize," Michael responded. "In Swift the neurotic scientists worry about the sun dying out, so they have to devise frantic schemes to extract sunbeams out of cucumbers to save the world. In our time the obsessed intellectuals are exercised over population explosions, so they invent judicial decisions and concoct laws of the land to kill babies and the elderly. In Swift mad architects build houses by constructing the roof first and then laying the foundation. In our day we propose to build the great edifice of society by destroying the family, the building block. In Swift the intellectuals live on a flying island up in the clouds removed from Mother Earth and divorced from reality. In our times the pundits and professors also live in an imaginary tower separated from all the accumulated wisdom of the entire world—a make-believe world where men and women are the same, where pregnancy is a disease, where children are a pestilence, where cloning humans is enlightened higher knowledge, and where good is evil and evil is good."

"Well," said Stepan, "during this vacation we're going to leave this mad world of big lies, imaginary worlds, and political correctness for a while and enter an older, saner, more human world—a world of memories that brings you into contact with the nature of things, the way things really are, the perennial truths that never change. Growing up in America in the 1940's and 1950's and recalling the old-world culture of Armenia that Mom and Dad brought to these shores and breathed into our lives is the best antidote to the mad world you describe, Tomas and Michael. It will be good for our children to compare and contrast the old and the new as we tell our stories and see how drastically the world changes for the worse when the wisdom of the ages is ignored.   I'm looking forward to tonight. When it gets dark, let's gather in my cabin. If the children sit on the floor and you all bring some chairs from your cottages, we'll be comfortably gathered for the story I'm calling 'The Miraculous Escape.'"

"All right," Melanie decided, "let's plan on our potluck supper at 6:00 at the picnic tables. The men will have the fire ready for the barbecue. I'll bring the paper plates and cups, and the older children will help me clean up afterwards. At nine o'clock we'll have real entertainment, much better than anything Hollywood or ABC would offer."

CHAPTER FOUR

Sunday Night: An Armenian Boy Versus the Turkish Army

"Tonight I'm going to begin the storytelling," Stepan began, "with a story you all know in part, the biography of our founding father. All you children know about the Turkish massacre of the Armenians during World War I from your parents, and you know that Grandpa Nubar escaped this tragedy, emigrated to the United States, worked as a locksmith in Milford, Massachusetts, where your parents, aunts, and uncles lived until their college years. But I'm not sure you know all the sequence of events or have all the facts. Let me tell you the whole story. I heard it from Grandpa in parts. and finally I pieced it together. I marvel at this story every time I think about or tell it. This is my story and your story too, not just the biography of Grandpa. It will help you understand why Armenians cherish the preciousness of life."

Stepan continued, "In the village of Agun your grandfather Nubar lived with his mother, a widow, and his younger sister Nunia He was about thirteen or fourteen years old. He was the fourth of five children, his three older brothers having left the old country for America or France to find jobs and find opportunities. One day the Turkish army entered the village and ordered the people to gather all their possessions and to prepare to relocate for purposes of safety because of the war. Of course it was an enormous lie. It was a trick to lead the Armenians in caravans through the mountains and deserts and then rob them, starve them, kill them, or let them die of exhaustion.

"The Turkish soldiers and the Kurds from the mountains plundered and looted the Armenians, seizing any of the possessions they wanted, checking all their clothes for money, jewels, or prized belongings. After a few days of marching it became perfectly clear to everyone that they were destined to die in the desert of Der-el-Zor or at the hands of Turkish soldiers. Grandpa mentioned the horrible memories of death he saw everywhere around him, shocked at the sight of women jumping into rivers with their babies rather than suffer the heat and torture any longer or the cruelties of the Turks. I remember Grandpa mentioned his disgust at the smell of human bodies left unburied by the soldiers and the horror of seeing so many bodies thrown in the rivers. Yes, I know, these details are loathsome and depressing to hear, but you're all old enough now to understand these things. This is just one reason why people refer to the 'ugliness' of sin and evil. We should never forget—the whole world should never forget—how gross and repulsive evil always is no matter how much lies, words, and propaganda attempt to deny it.

"So one evening as the march through the desert continues, Grandpa's mother Yeranoui (Evelyn) told her son, 'I want to tell you something. You must listen and promise to do it. It is nighttime now. When we wind around the next mountain in the darkness, I want you to run. Yes, *hokees* (my beloved one), you and Kevork, your best friend, have a chance to escape if you run fast under the cover of the dark and stay in the back of the march. The gendarmes may see you, but they cannot chase you; you can easily outrun them. They may fire, but they will not see their target. You must take this chance. I want you to do this. I am your mother, and I don't want you to be killed or die in the desert. It will be better than walking to our deaths on this march. The Turks are going to kill every last one of us somehow. I cannot run like you, and I must stay with Nunia. It is better that one of us should live than all of us go to our deaths.'

Nubar listened to his mother. Her strong words came from her heart. She loved her son so much that she was desperate

I want to tell you something. You must listen and promise to do it. It is nighttime now. When we wind around the next mountain in the darkness, I want you to run. Yes, hokees (my beloved one), you and Kevork, your best friend, have a chance to escape if you run fast under the cover of the dark and stay in the back of the march.

to save him any way she could. She would rather have him take this wild chance than continue with her and his sister to certain death. Nubar knew his mother was right; he knew her pleas were the words of a mother's love. He knew he could outrun every soldier. With Kevork beside him they could figure out what to do afterwards, where to hide, where to go. So the two boys began to linger toward the end of the caravan. When the path began to wind, your great grandmother Yeranouhi tapped Nubar and said "Heema!" (Now!) Nubar and Kevork ran wildly down the slope and ignored all the shouts and threats of the soldiers who fired several shots in the distance in vain. When they finally stopped running about ten minutes later and looked backwards, they heard no footsteps and saw no movements. The guards probably thought that two runaway boys no doubt would die of starvation or be caught by other Turkish gendarmes. In any case, the chase was over, and the boys were alive.

"For the next year to year and a half—I'm not sure of the exact period of time—Grandpa and his friend Kevork lived like vagabonds, hiding during the day, stealing fruit from orchards wherever possible, living outdoors, starving for food much of the time. Once he was so desperate that he ate grass to curb his raging hunger. He became seriously ill and remained very sick for a long time because of this craving for anything to satisfy his stomach. In any case, Grandpa lived like this—running and hiding, foraging for any kind of food, and struggling to survive—until the Armistice was signed in 1918 that officially ended World War I. Grandpa just remembers this period as a constant cry of hunger. A fourteen-year-old orphan living like an animal and being always on guard, feeling hunted, and wondering if his mother and sister could possibly be alive, he was haunted by the nightmarish deaths he witnessed and the terror of being absolutely alone in a hostile, diabolical world.

"After the Armistice he found his way back to his village of Agun. When he returned, he was recognized by a schoolteacher who wanted to give him an important letter. His two older brothers in America, Tavit and Aris, had received news of the genocide of the Armenians; newspapers were reporting stories about "the starving Armenians." United States ambassador Morgenthau wrote that the Turks perpetrated the most sadistic and perverse forms of cruelty and torture ever invented by the most diabolical imagination. The Armenians in America knew what their countrymen were suffering in the old country. Trying to save their family, Grandpa's older brothers had sent money for their mother, brother, and sister to purchase boat tickets to come to America and escape the violence in Turkey. They heard no news about the fate of the family in Turkey but hoped they were still alive. It was shortly after Grandpa Nubar's return to the village that the teacher found him and brought him the letter with the money. With no members of his family remaining in Agun and after the terror of the death march he had suffered, Grandpa rushed immediately to escape this living hell. For his journey to America he had to travel by wagon from the village of Agun to the port at Istanbul where he would board the ship that would bring him to Ellis Island in New York. Remember that he is just about fourteen years old as he is undergoing this nightmare of unspeakable evil. Now he is to travel across the ocean entirely by himself to a foreign country.

The schoolteacher, a friend of the family, helped the young Nubar find a ride to Istanbul. Two Turkish drivers drove their wagon regularly along the roads leading to the port and agreed to take the boy to the seacoast. Of course Grandpa had to pretend he was Turkish, or his life might be in danger again. The hatred of many of the Turks toward the Armenians ("*giaour*" or infidel they called them) threatened innocent Armenians who happened to be at the mercy of those Turks who believed they were going to their heaven for killing in the name of their religion. Grandpa could speak Turkish as fluently as Armenian, and so the two Turks at first did not suspect that he was an Armenian. This trip to Istanbul took a few days and required sleeping outdoors for the night. One night when the two drivers assumed Grandpa was sound asleep, they began talking. One of the Turks said, 'You know, I think he's a filthy *giaour*, I'll bet on it. I'm going to kill him—tonight! While he is sound asleep! With my sword! It's so easy. Right here in the dead of night, far away from everything.'

"But the other driver objected: 'So what if he's an Armenian? Yes, we could find out for sure whether he is Christian or Moslem—very easily done! I don't care whether or not he's a *giaour*. He is just an innocent, just a boy. Leave him alone! I'm not having any killing! We're here to do our job—nothing else. Say no more! Drive those thoughts out of your mind! I don't want anything to do with it. Do you understand?'

"The murderous Turk dropped the idea: 'Forget it!' he finally said and changed the topic of conversation, turning his thoughts to other things. Grandpa pretended he was sound asleep but overheard much of the conversation. Again he was that close to the jaws of death, but through the mercy of God and the kind heart of the good Turk his life was spared a second time. In any case Grandpa finally relaxed enough to fall asleep. They continued the journey the next day and finally arrived at their destination. Grandpa reached Istanbul and boarded the ship for America.

"All he remembers about this long journey from one part of the world to another across an endless ocean is that he slept on a barrel each night. Yes, that's right: he slept on a barrel! As one of the lowest class passengers, he had no cabin or any other type of sleeping quarters. He was entirely on his own to improvise or find some place on the ship to put his sleepy head. Can you believe this? Fourteen years old! No father and no mother! Nearly starved to death! Orphaned! Destitute! Horrified by the disgusting cruelty of Turks wantonly killing innocent people! And now traveling alone across oceans and sleeping on a barrel! That's our father and our grandfather. That's how our family came to America, and that's the beginning of our history in this country. I took a long time telling it, but all you grandchildren should know and remember this story.

"Never take the gift of life for granted. It's a miracle we are alive, and only by the grace of God are we here today. We would never have been born if Grandpa died on the march or was slaughtered by the vicious Turk. Just think: what if Grandpa's mother did not beg him to run? What if Grandpa was too afraid to run and decided to stay and face death with his mother and sister? What if there were no kind Turk to protest the savage killing of an innocent orphan? When you know all the facts about your family history or the great events in your parents' lives, you then begin to understand the mysterious hand of God's Divine Providence in human life. Don't forget: your grandfather's escape from death is a miracle. Your lives are also a miracle. The survival of the Armenian people is also another great miracle," Uncle Stepan concluded as he addressed all the grandchildren.

"What a heartbreaking, moving, powerful story!" Michael's daughter Talene remarked. "That poor man! Now I understand why he often said that he went from living in hell in Turkey to living in heaven in America. Also do you remember the time, Dad, that Grandpa was visiting us during one summer? You asked him if you could pose some questions about his life and record his answers on audiotape; you turned on the tape recorder when the two of you started talking. I still remember the final question and the answer. You said, 'Well, Dad, you have not said anything in Armenian; so far you have answered all my questions in English. Why don't you end by saying something in Armenian.' Grandpa answered, '*Hokees goodum haires yev maires vor desnum*'('I would give my heart and soul to see my father and mother'). As an orphan who lost his father as a child and had no memory of him and as a young boy who was violently separated from his mother never to see her again, I can imagine how great was his longing to know and be with his parents. There he was in his 70's, and what was foremost in his mind? His heartsickness for mother and father. And yet what a good, devoted father he obviously was even though he never knew a normal home life after he left Turkey. My heart breaks every time I think of all he suffered at such a young age."

Melanie's son Vahan also reacted. "When you hear a story like that," he began, "it inspires you with courage and patience— what a heroic life! If Grandpa could suffer all that mental and physical pain, then it makes you realize that you too can draw from those deepest resources you have within yourself. Knowing something about his life, I can't tell how many times his example has influenced me. When I compete in track and cross-country, I sometimes feel ready to give up and not push myself any further, but I think of Grandpa and then feel a surge of energy. When some of my college courses—like calculus and organic chemistry— become demanding and the subject matter overwhelms me, I'm tempted to stop trying—especially after a disappointing grade— but I think of Grandpa's persistence, perseverance, and will power, and then I suddenly feel stronger and more committed. No matter what happened in his life, he never gave up. That's what I love! No such thing as a 'To be or not to be' soliloquy for Grandpa Nubar. I remember once when he was reviewing some parts of his life, one of the grandchildren said, 'Grandpa, I can't believe you never quit, did you? You never stopped trying. You never gave up hope. You never lost your will to live or fight against odds.' And that was Grandpa's great lesson. He would say, 'No, never, never quit!' "

"Whenever I think of my father's life," Anahid intervened, "I always think of the Church's teaching about the inestimable value of each and every life, the preciousness of every human being, God's love for each single soul. Here you have this supposedly worthless "*giaour*" ready to be slaughtered like a cow or pig by the Turks—an orphan or 'unwanted child' as he would be called today by the pro-abortion ideologues—whose life is unbelievably transformed from darkness into light. He was supposed to be killed, and he rose from the dead. He was despicable and hated by the Turks but beloved and honored by his children and grandchildren. Just think of all that God can do with one human life! Not someone with advantages, special talents, a superior education, or extraordinary genius. Just a simple, ordinary boy from an obscure village in rural Turkish Armenia. All this goodness, happiness, and joy that was poured into our lives and our children's lives through Grandpa Nubar fighting to survive, struggling to find his way in a new world, and eventually marrying and founding a family. Here we are, five families and all these grandchildren, in awe that we are here alive rejoicing in life and thankful for our marriages and families. Whoever would have imagined this on that fateful day when the Turkish army entered the village of Agun and ordered the people to march? What a testimony to the virtue of Christian hope! Really, 'the future does not have to resemble the past'. Didn't Augustine say this? I never cease to be amazed that good can come out of evil."

"Well, that's why it's dangerous for man to try to play God and become the arbiter of life or death," Michael added. "We think that government, science, and medicine have all the answers about matters of life or death, and so the question of who lives and who dies is determined, not by a recognition of the dignity of each and every person as an image of God, but by cost effectiveness, quality of life, usefulness and productivity, and some perverse idea of choice. Who knows what God has in store for each individual? Who can ever predict how the hand of Divine Providence will intervene and transform someone's life? Some sociologist would have predicted that Dad would grow up in poverty, turn to crime, be a burden to society, or end up in jail. So much for human infallibility!"

Melanie entered the conversation: "Do you know what I can't quite understand? I can't fathom how any member of a race or a nation that has suffered a holocaust or a genocide could possibly be neutral or hostile to the pro-life cause in our times. How can you know first-hand the horror of mass executions or pogroms and then vote for Democratic candidates who are pro-abortion, even pro-infanticide—which is exactly what partial-birth abortion is. I can't believe how any Armenian could in good conscience belong to the Democratic party and consistently elect pro-abortion politicians. Also I'm just as appalled that Jews are so liberal in their views on abortion. Somehow no one wants to see the hard truth: abortion is the genocide or holocaust of our times. When we see the visual evidence of Nazi war crimes and watch shocking movies like SCHINDLER'S LIST, we are horrified at the unspeakable nature of this evil, but no newspapers or television shows ever dare show us the pictures of aborted babies. All I know is that every Armenian family and every Jewish family especially should be passionately pro-life."

"Uncle Stepan," said Tomas's daughter Seta , "thank

you so much for thinking of this reunion and convincing everyone to come. I'm so glad everyone is here. What a great time we're going to have! I confess I wasn't thrilled at the idea of passing the evenings in storytelling. I thought it would just be old-timers reminiscing and recalling 'the good old days,' but this is a treat."

It was evident that Stepan's poignant story spoke to the hearts of the cousins. Their eyes reflected an intent, spellbound look of awe. They felt like crying for their grandfather, who was deprived of so much in life that is precious but managed to provide so generously for his own children: a stable, permanent home; a mother and a father's love; a true childhood and life of innocence, and the privilege of an education.

"Uncle Mike," added Seta's sister Arpine, "I just love this idea of getting to know about everyone's life by hearing their favorite stories. You get to know a person not only by what he does and says but also by what he enjoys—his favorite stories, sayings, music, and books. I remember a job interview where I was asked 'What book or author has most influenced your thinking and philosophy of life?' At the time we were studying THE CANTERBURY TALES in a literature class, and that was my answer. Why? Because it is about all of life from tragedy to comedy, about all of human nature from saints to villains and from the wise to the foolish. There is all this human interaction between knights, merchants, and lawyers, between men and women, and between the old and the young. That to me is life, the real thing. I can feel that is already happening here.

"Well, then," said Stepan, "let's taste all of life and go from the tragic to the comic. Who wants to go next? Tonight's story was grim and chilling, but it's the logical one for the clan to hear first. Let's have a change of pace for tomorrow night. Any volunteers?"

"Oh, I know," uttered Anahid's son Gregory. "I'll never forget this episode; in fact, I even wrote about it in class, and I brought a copy of the story. Can I read it instead of telling it?"

"Great," responded Uncle Stepan to his nephew. "Sure, go right ahead and read it. A good story is a good story whether it's read or told. Tomorrow we will alternate storytellers from an old-timer to the young at heart and move from the grave to the lighthearted. Tomorrow night will be devoted to the comic spirit. You are our bard and entertainment for Monday night, Greg. The muse of Chaucer will inspire our storytelling with his spirit."

The mood was successfully set for the Bedrosian reunion. Everyone had his fill of the good things of the day—the fresh air and the beach, laughter and fun, abundant and delicious food, and conversation and wisdom. Young and old enjoyed each other's company, the older members of the family animated by the spirit and humor of the young and the younger members enriched by the experience and wisdom of their elders. Everyone was looking forward to the next day. Seta had used the right expression: "all this human interaction." It was all so natural and normal but yet so untypical and rare. When Seta used that phrase, her cousin Gregory thought of the infrequency of this type of communication. The pictures in his mind were people listening to the same radio station in their cars, families watching the same television stations in their homes, the average person reading the same newspapers every day, and college students listening to the same slogans about 'dead white men,' 'patriarchy as the root of all evil,' 'a woman's right to choice,' and 'diversity.' He saw this distinction clearly: the carefully controlled flow of information and images received through the official channels of NBC, THE NEW YORK TIMES, and Hollywood versus the dynamic, spirited exchange of families talking about a myriad of topics in the most open, free, spirited manner where everyone's wise or foolish opinion is heard from Mom and Dad's to little brother's. Information can issue from a tube, a television circuit, or a telephone line or overflow from the cornucopia of human interaction in a family. Gregory was beginning to experience this feast of knowledge that real experience brings to good stories and to recognize how infrequent this exchange occurs in modern life. He had read some of THE CANTERBURY TALES in college but never considered them in the light in which Arpine described the book: 'all this human interaction.'

CHAPTER FIVE

Monday Night: The Tale of the Grandmother Who Couldn't Sleep

Greg looked forward to reciting his story. He remembered this episode as if it were yesterday, and he laughed so hard when he wrote about the incident for an English composition class. He was laughing to himself at the thought of re-living the experience as he retold it to all the relatives. How vividly he remembered these occasions when relatives visited the home and he felt the enrichment of belonging to a large, extended family. How distinctive and unique each of his relatives were, especially Grandma Elise. Already he was beginning to chuckle at another comic scene that occurred during the same time as the adventure in the story. Grandma Elise was accustomed to reading daily newspapers and hearing news on television several times a day. When she visited Anahid and Dickran in Iowa, she was in a bit of culture shock at the fact that they did not own a television or subscribe to a newspaper. "What's the matter with you people?" she would complain. "Don't you want to know what's happening in the world or know the weather for the next day?" Because Anahid and Dickran were avid readers and busy reading to their children or playing with them, they never desired a television. "We were getting a newspaper," Anahid explained. "But neither one of us was reading it; we were just wasting our money. We just turn on the radio for the news and weather at breakfast time if we feel an interest."

Grandma found her daughter and son-in-law strange, to

say the least. But when you are in Rome, you do as the Romans do. After some minor withdrawal symptoms, she quickly became accustomed to more conversation and less television, more sewing and cooking than listening to news. The relaxed, serene pace of Iowa was lulling her into a peace of mind that her life in Massachusetts did not allow. Shortly before her scheduled departure date, Grandma had received a telephone call from her sister Rose who was planning to meet her at Logan Airport in Boston. "So, Elise, what are you going to do?"

"What am I going to do? About what? What are you talking about? No, I haven't heard. They don't even have a television here, and no one even buys a newspaper. What? No!" You should have seen Grandma's reaction. I can still hear her: "See! I told you people! You never get any news, you don't know what's happening anyplace, and now my sister has to call me from Massachusetts to tell me that my flight from Iowa is cancelled! There's an airline strike. Ooof! Now what am I supposed to do? You people need to get newspapers and have a television!" And so the relaxing vacation to Iowa suddenly became a headache, and Grandma's prophecy proved true.

As Greg prepared everyone for Monday night's story, he had also told them about this comic interlude as an appetizer. Now he began in earnest "The Tale of the Grandmother Who Couldn't Sleep":

"There was once a sweet, gentle, loving grandmother who lived in a big, crowded city in Massachusetts. Every summer night when she tried to fall asleep, some noise from the city, the street, or the neighborhood woke her up. One night she heard the sirens of the fire engines that raced through the city and startled her from her happy dreams. Another time the loud noises of a motorcycle ruined her deep, peaceful sleep. Whenever Grandmother was awakened by these sudden noises, she could not fall asleep again. So when she finally left her bed in the morning, she was often grouchy and irritable.

"Sometimes—once in a great while—grandmother would sleep through the whole night. But then she was jolted from her relaxing sleep by her next-door neighbor who started his car early in the morning and kept it running for a long time. The two houses were very close to each other in this crowded city. 'I need to get some good sleep,' said Grandmother, 'or I will be the world's worst grouch. I know! I have a great idea! I'll go and visit my daughter Anahid and my son-in-law Dickran in Iowa. Besides, I miss my dear grandchildren. They live in quiet, peaceful, rural Iowa. There in Iowa I know I won't hear so many sirens, motorcycles, and noisy cars, for Iowa is not crowded and congested like Massachusetts. It has big farms where all is calm and still at night. Oh! I can hardly wait.'

"Grandmother had made up her mind. She made her airline reservation, and in a week's time she was on her way to the Midwest to enjoy a quiet vacation in peaceful Iowa where she would welcome the sweetest sleep of the night. She had a wonderful time the first day, hearing all the grandchildren tell her about school, soccer, piano, and the dog Lucky. At night when all the children were getting ready for bed, Grandma also felt exhausted. She could hardly wait to collapse in bed and enjoy a long, sweet Iowa sleep. The neighborhood appeared perfectly quiet. All day she had heard no noisy cars, roaring motorcycles, or screeching sirens. Grandma soon drifted into a deep sleep and thought she was in the Land of Nod. She was dreaming happily and floating on clouds when suddenly she was roused by the piercing sounds of a barking dog in the yard of the next-door neighbor: 'Ruff! Ruff! Ruff!'. The noise grew louder and sharper.

"The family dog Lucky also stirred at the sound of another dog and began yelping himself as he ran back and forth from the back door to the front door and then to the back door again. The neighbor's dog Shotzie was acting crazily, sounding wilder and more excited each second. 'Yip! Yip Yip!' he repeated, which was dog language for 'Lucky! Hurry! Come quickly! A rabbit is in my yard. I saw it, and I smell it. Let's chase it before it gets away. I need you right now.'

"Lucky understood Shotzie's sounds perfectly and began barking hysterically. In dog language he reassured Shotzie he was coming. To stop the barking, my father finally let the dog out so that the whole household would not be awake. But the damage was done. Grandma's sleep was spoiled, never to return again for the night. In Massachusetts it was sirens and motorcycles; in Iowa it was dogs and rabbits. Of course the next day Grandma was a bit grouchy and cranky because that's what happens when a person does not get enough rest.

"The next night Grandma hoped for a better night's sleep. Very tired and weary, she fell asleep instantly and began to go into a deep slumber. Shotzie and Lucky also were dead tired, and all the children were nestled in their beds: 'Not a creature was stirring, not even a mouse.' But just as Grandma was falling deeper and deeper into a long rest, her four-year-old grandson Levon was beginning to wake up. He began to talk in his sleep, then whimper, and then cry aloud, 'Daddy, Mommy, come sleep with me. I had a bad dream.' Levon's loud sobs and calls in the middle of the night aroused his three-year-old sister Lucy. Suddenly jolted from her sleep, Lucy screamed and roared. Soon all the children were awake and talking. Dad rushed to comfort Levon, and Mom ran to quiet Lucy. So much for Grandmother's sweet Iowa sleep on the second night!

"Poor Grandmother! First it was the dogs; then it was the grandchildren. She wondered if anyone in any part of the country ever enjoyed a good night's sleep. Did all the devils and demons come out at night just to ruin a person's needed rest? Maybe her home in Massachusetts and her own bed were the best place for sleepless grandmothers after all. She would try one more time. To be sure, three wishes are a magical number in folktales. Surely, she thought, there can't be rabbits exciting dogs or dreams awakening children every single night! Those were just odd happenings, not normal occurrences. So once again Grandma attempted to close her eyes and experience a Rip Van Winkle sleep. Her wishes were beginning to come true, for this night there were no dogs barking or children crying. But who can ever foresee all the enemies of sleep who are always hovering and ready to attack the innocent rest of the weary? Who would have ever guessed it?

"A burst of sound that exploded like gunfire suddenly forced Grandma to sit up in bed. The rain poured heavily, making loud, beating sounds on the roof directly above her. The thunder seemed to burst again and again, leaving Grandma so wide awake that all she could do was to wait for the morning. 'I'll just have to wait until I return to Massachusetts to get my sleep,' Grandma sighed. 'I guess I made a mistake; I thought Iowa was a quiet place. At least that's what everyone told me.'

"It was soon that Grandmother said good-bye to everyone and left for Massachusetts. She loved every moment of her vacation in Iowa but came to dread the nights. She began to miss her favorite bed and old home. All she could think about when she boarded the plane was the sweet sleep that awaited her in familiar surroundings. That night in her own house in her own bedroom in her own bed she thought of Iowa. As she remembered the dogs barking, the children crying, and the thunder clapping, she fell asleep in a wink and did not hear the fire engines, motor cycles, and loud cars that raced and screeched outside her windows."

"Did that all really happen, Greg?" asked his cousin Aram. "Your story reminded me of a Jewish folktale that Mom and Dad read to us over and over again. They felt crowded in their small house and were constantly complaining about the lack of space. Then they brought the dog, cat, birds, and many creatures into their house so that there was no room anyplace. After a period of time they let all the animals go outside again and marveled at their spacious, comfortable home."

"I remember it vividly, but you can ask my mother and father," replied Greg. "I know that the three things in the story really happened—dogs yelping one night, then Levon and Lucy crying in the middle of the night, and finally the thunderstorm."

"Of course, it really happened," Anahid interjected. "That story is a wonderful introduction to rock-bottom reality—a true reflection of family life. You quickly learn as a parent with young children that life is 'a chaos worth living.' That was the expression my literature professor used when we were discussing Shakespeare's comedies and Chaucer's tales. I always liked that phrase because it is so honest. So many people experience the chaotic part of living, and many religious authors write about life as worth living, but family life illustrates the actual combination of the two. Nothing is more comical than family life, and no one is more surprising than young children. Nothing ever goes exactly like planned, and even going to bed at night can be extraordinarily eventful."

"That's for sure," Melanie continued. "In fact, we coined a term in our family called 'family fiascoes.' Here we are shopping in the mall and one of the children has the urge to go to the restroom. So we rush to the nearest place that is likely to have one—a business that looks like a restaurant. 'Sir, which way is the bathroom?'—a simple, innocent question, right? This is the answer I get: 'Mam, this is a pub; no children are allowed here. I could get fined if anyone reports that a child is in here.' What can I say?

"All I can do is plead and beg with my eyes: 'Sir, this is *very* urgent; my son can't wait.' The bartender answers, 'M'am, go ahead, but please don't let anyone see you. I could lose my license. Just turn to the right.' What a narrow escape by the skin of our teeth!

"Breathing a sigh of relief, I rejoin my husband and other children, feeling I can now relax and do some shopping. But oh no! Now my daughter says, 'Mommy, I have to go to the bathroom too.' So where is the nearest restroom? Of course it's the one in the pub. Now what do I do? This time I hold my breath and walk right past the bar and head for the bathroom. Let's hope the bartender doesn't see me. What do I say if he notices me and stops me after he warned me and pleaded with me never ever to do this again? I just held my breath and walked in and out as if I were doing the most normal thing in the world—running into the pub with my children as if it were my natural destination and doing it over and over again."

"By the way, speaking of family fiascos, we have a funny story to tell also," said Aunt Siran, Tomas's wife. "Is this a good time, or is it getting late?"

"Oh, please go ahead and tell it, Aunt Siran," several of the nieces and nephews insisted. "Everyone's in the mood tonight for comedy." So the comic muse prevailed, Uncle Stepan gave his approval, and Uncle decided this would be the last story of the night.

Aunt Siran explained that their tale would be entitled "A Day of Learning at Kansas University" and that it was based on the time she and Tomas visited Michael and Anna in Lawrence, Kansas.

She began: "You've all heard Mark Twain's famous statement: 'Truth is stranger than fiction.' This really happened, and I'm not embellishing or exaggerating. After you heard of the fiasco of rushing children to the restrooms in the pub—historical fact—you'll know that our story is just as realistic and credible, thanks to our ever spontaneous and surprising children.

"Since we were spending part of our Easter vacation at a large university, Tomas and I decided we should have an outing and see the sights and provide our children the benefits of culture. So we plan on touring the beautiful grounds of the university, visiting the museum of history, and seeing the paintings in the art gallery. It sounds like a delightful idea, doesn't it, a perfect way to do something together as a family, right? When Tomas mentions the schedule of activities for the day to the children, he of course mentions that we will finish our tour with a snack at the Kansas Union.

"Since our four-year-old daughter Seta did not eat much for breakfast, I naturally pack a bag of snack foods for her to keep her from complaining. Our first stop is the museum of history. As we open the door to begin our tour, a big, bold, clear sign stares at us: 'Absolutely no food or drink permitted' it says. As we begin looking at old Eskimo harpoons and Indian weapons, Seta does not seem interested in history one bit. 'Mommy, I want a snack,' she whines; 'Daddy, I want a snack,' she repeats and repeats.

" 'No, Seta,' Tomas explains, 'we can't eat here. See that big sign. It says we can't eat here. We have to wait until we leave and go outside.' Dad's logic has no effect on his daughter. Seta's voice becomes louder and louder, more and more demanding. It just so happens that we are the only people in the museum at 10:00 a.m., and so all the staff and all the janitors are staring at us. Yes, we are getting embarrassed and a little angry. If she had just eaten her breakfast! In the meantime our nine-year-old Harry is pointing to the skulls of Neanderthal man to his five-year-old brother Ara: 'Ara, Ara, come here!' Harry shouts. 'Harry, what's that?' Ara wonders. Harry acts like an expert: 'Ara, that's what happens to you when you die; you turn into a skeleton and a skull!'

"Ara, looking puzzled, uncertain, and afraid, turns to Tomas with anxiety: 'Daddy, when I die, I won't be like that, will I? My skull will be in heaven, won't it?' This is a hard question for a wise father to answer, even for one who never runs out of explanations. Tomas stammers, 'Don't worry, Ara; you'll be in heaven for sure.' Tomas changes the subject quickly: 'Come here, Ara; let's look at that Indian tomahawk.'

"We're lucky that this is not a very big museum, for we're able to finish our tour quickly. Now we can make Seta happy. As soon as we step outdoors, I hand her a box of raisins and a cracker. 'Mom, do you have any more snacks?' asks Harry. 'I want a snack too,' insists Ara. During the first five minutes after we leave the museum and walk toward the next building, all the boxes of raisins and crackers are devoured, and it's only an hour since breakfast!

"Tomas thinks we will enjoy hiking around Potter's Lake that is part of the campus. So we begin walking slowly up a big hill to see this sight. As we approach the water, Harry spies an old can floating close to shore and notices the tall reeds that are a foot or two into the water. Before we realize it, all the children are at the water's edge bending as far as they can to reach their treasure. 'Come over here!' I yell. 'Don't step in the water! Leave that stupid can alone! Quick, you're going to fall in!' Yes, Tomas thought they would enjoy the beauty of the lake, but they found the old can much more interesting.

"Then Dad wanted to show us Kansas University's football stadium where the great Gale Sayers ran for many breakaway touchdowns. We start to head in that direction, but Harry finds an old golf ball along the way. He starts to bounce it and roll it down the steep hills of the campus. So now all the children are fascinated by an old golf ball racing down the slope of a hill, and not a soul cares about the lake, the stadium, or any of the great learning and culture KU offers.

"We had decided to finish our trip with a snack at the Kansas Union. As we are walking in that direction, we notice that the art museum is in the same direction and close by. Tomas turns to the children, 'Look, there is the art museum. Wouldn't you like to see some paintings and drawings in all kinds of colors,' hoping they will all yell yes. 'Besides,' he says to me, 'we may never have this chance again. We might as well.' Nobody complains or objects as we proceed to the building.

"When Ara and Seta learn that they are going on an elevator, they become excited and competitive: 'I want to push the button! I want to push the button!' they both shout simultaneously. To prevent an argument, I promise Seta that she can press the button when we go up and tell Ara he can push the button when we come down. End of argument.

"Up to the third level we go. As we are about to leave the elevator, Seta does not want to get off. She begins whining, 'I want to go on the elevator again. Let's go up some more. Let's go down now.' As she is pouting just outside the elevator, Ara notices two security guards standing with uniforms before an entrance gate with bars: 'Is that a jail, Mom? How come they have police?' Dad reassures Ara that this is not a prison, explaining, 'These men are guards. Their job is to tell people not to touch those old pieces of furniture and those beautiful paintings. So be careful. Don't touch anything, please.' But Seta can't remember or refuses to understand. The guards follow us everywhere we go, reiterating more than once to the children, 'Don't touch! Don't touch!' and apologizing to us, 'I know it's rough on the children, but that's our job.' It's time to leave, not enjoy art.

"As we leave the third floor of the museum, Ara and Seta love the thought of touching elevator buttons again. After we land on the fourth level, Seta stops thinking about elevators and is reminded of something else. Tomas and the guards burst out laughing when Seta says as loudly and nervously as possible, 'Is this a doctor's office?' she felt certain that she was going to see a doctor and started feeling nervous about the thought of getting a shot in the arm. 'Let's go home! I want to go home!' Seta began whining.No one could figure out why an art museum reminded a little girl of a doctor's office. It must have have been the neat, clean, polished, antiseptic look or some smell in the air. I guess museums are no fun for four-year-old little girls who like snacks and shun doctors' offices.

"One last stop–the Kansas Union for some cookies and apple juice to end the day's outing on a positive note. All of us enjoy the treat and a chance to rest from all our walking. Our adventure is just about over. In about ten minutes we will all be back home. However, just as we are about to leave the cafeteria, Seta spills her apple juice and feels the wetness on her clothing. 'Mommy, change my pants; change my pants, Mommy'. We have not gone to the beach, and so there's no dry clothing in supply.

"Seta then turns to her father: 'Daddy, change my pants. My pants are all wet,' she continues to repeat in a half-whining, half-crying tone. Tomas does not know what to say or do. As we are leaving the Kansas Union and step outside, the sun breaks through the clouds and begins shining for the first time that day. 'Look, Seta,' Dad says, 'the sun is shining; the warm sun will dry your pants.' My little girl begins smiling again and says cheerfully, 'Mommy, the sun will dry my pants.'

"That was our famous day of learning in the halls of higher education at Kansas University. We don't remember what we saw or learned in the museum, art gallery, or tour. But we will never forget the box of raisins, the old can in the lake, the elevator buttons, and the apple-juice pants," Siran concluded.

"How could you remember all that, Aunt Siran?" asked her niece Mariam.

"How could you forget it, Miriam?' replied her aunt. 'When you are hoping and planning one thing and exactly the opposite happens, do you think you could forget even one detail? Suppose you were planning your wedding in June and hoped for beautiful weather, but then a hurricane or tornado dashed all your hopes–do you think you would forget any part of that day? Probably not."

"Now do all you cousins realize why your parents have

such highly developed senses of humor," interjected Melanie. "You might get upset at your first or second family fiasco, but after that all you can do is laugh, smile, and be lighthearted. When they happen, write them down. They provide wonderful material for letters, and, as you can see, they are the essence of family reunions. Also when your children develop airs, it's good to recount these stories. They keep everyone down-to-earth. Children learn humility when their parents retell these tales, and parents learn not to take themselves so seriously, not to have grandiose plans. And so when children grow up and become parents and remember these stories, they gain perspective. Family fiascos keep both parents and children in line, don't you think?"

"Absolutely," insisted Michael's wife Anna. "I was just reading the other day something by Chesterton that I loved. He said that a mother at home with children has a more thorough grasp of reality and the nature of things than the most educated philosopher. That's so true. We know what to expect; we know what's possible; we are very realistic; we don't live up in the air. We know all about stubborn wills, lazy wills, disobedient wills, and uncontrollable wills. We are experts on human nature. We know all about theories of raising children that haven't an ounce of experience behind them. Children teach us these facts of life very quickly. The simplest things—like going on a family trip—can become complicated problems. The easiest, most natural things—like eating, sleeping, or sharing—can be major issues. We know all about fallen man and original sin, don't we, mothers?"

"Oh, yes we do," agreed Siran. "So we know what our job is—to civilize human beings, and that means not only good manners and good morals but also fun, laughter, and good times. Yes, we have to insist on cleanliness, table etiquette, and proper clothing, but we also like outings and adventures outside the home. We like order, but it has to be a human order—not a mechanical or rigid one. So what if elaborate plans turn into family fiascos? We understand the virtue of flexibility. C'est la vie. We teach our children and husbands to learn to relax and not be so straitlaced or scheduled. Life comes before schedules."

"Do you know, in today's culture you rarely hear about the comedy of children or the zaniness of family fiascos," commented Michael. "It's one of those suppressed truths like the comedy of marriage. We hear about the burden of children, the cost of children, unwanted children, but it's all too uncommon to hear about a baby entertaining a whole family in the living room. How often do you see a universal experience like that in Hollywood films, popular culture, or contemporary literature. Gone too is the sense of humor between men and women, the banter, the repartee, the joking. That's half the fun in marriage."

"You're right," added Tomas. "Part of the happiness in marriage is the ability to laugh at each other and yourself—to see yourself as a comic creature as your spouse does. I remember the last time we took a vacation Siran insisted that the house be immaculately clean. Here we are packing, getting ready, trying to remember to bring everything, loading the car, and my wife insists on scrubbing, vacuuming, and dusting just before we leave. I'm asking her, 'Why are we doing this now? We can clean after we come back, and besides we're not that usually thorough and impeccable in our ordinary cleaning. And we're not expecting guests. Why are we going crazy cleaning now when we should be leaving? Here is her answer.

"Siran says, 'I don't mind living in a state of semi-cleanliness or chaos. I know, I don't make the bed every day. But I *can't* leave and then come home to a messy house or an unmade bed!' Figure that out. This is the comedy of marriage. My wife is always making fun of my clothes selection. I am never perfectly color-coordinated. I wear the wrong style of shoe with my pants. My ties don't blend with my shirt or blazer. You see, we are sources of comedy for each other. Real family life develops this gift more than any other experience. Parents laugh at children, husbands and wives find each other amusing, and of course children are always exaggerating the faults of their parents to their friends and making them sound as odd and eccentric as possible."

"Come to think of it," added Michael, "many of the writers who loved the family were also the ones with robust senses of humor. Consider Dickens, Chesterton, and Saroyan. What lovable, funny characters in their stories: Betsy Trotwood in DAVID COPPERFIELD, Chesterton's hilarious comments on family life as "the wildest of adventures," and Saroyan's Mr. Ara, the Armenian grocer in THE HUMAN COMEDY who reminds me of so many of our relatives. How can you ever forget his remark, 'I no got cookies—raisins in.' Can I just read this? It's hilarious, and it's rooted in Armenian family life. Mr. Ara is a grocer who has all kinds of cookies in stock except the kind that a father wants for his sick son—raisin cookies. Trying hard to please his son and then his customer but feeling like a failure, Mr. Ara vents his frustration:

'Apples,' the grocer said, 'orange, candy, banana—no cookies. He's my boy. Three year old. Not sick. He want many things. He want apple. He want orange. He want candy. He want banana. I don't know what he want. He just want. He look at God. He say, Give me dis, give me dat—but he never satisfied. Always he want. He just want. Always he's feel bad. Poor God has got nothing for such sadness. He give everything—world—sunshine—moder—fader—broder—sister—onkle—cousin—house, farm, stove, table, bed—poor God give everything—but nobody happy—everybody like small boy sick with influenza—everybody say give me cookies—raisins in.' The grocer stopped a moment to take a very deep breath. When he exhaled he said very loudly to his customer, 'Is no cookies—raisins in.'

"It's one of the funniest scenes in THE HUMAN COMEDY, and it's the natural humor that always grows in loving homes," concluded Michael.

"The family is supposed to balance us," Anahid interjected. "That's what Mr. Ara is trying to do—bring everyone down to earth. That's the great benefit of humor and laughter too. In that way we avoid being so serious that we're grave, and we escape being so harum-scarum that we're jackasses. As children we need discipline, and we need love—the balance of the two. A family tells you your faults and then forgives them—a very healthy thing. Your father gives you justice and your mother gives you mercy—both conditional and unconditional love—and we need them both. Both boys and girls need to learn strength—will power—and also gentleness, sensitivity to another person's feelings. We learn them both from the combined influence of a father and mother, and so we become whole human beings. As the influence of the family declines, humans become unbalanced—heads without hearts, athletes without minds, geniuses without conscience, boys without honor, girls with no modesty. Families, humor, balance: they all go together. See, everyone, why the Bedrosians are all so perfectly normal, and you cousins thought we were a bit strange and—what was the expression I heard a few days ago?—a little 'north-north west.' It's the world that is mad, not us. Am I not right, Stepan, Michael, Melanie, Tomas?"

"Of course, you're always right," the other Bedrosians assented.

"Speaking of William Saroyan, families, and comedy," Melanie's husband Armen remarked, "do any of you know the story about Saroyan, his mother, and the victrola?" No one was familiar with it, so he briefly recounted it.

"Saroyan's mother Takoohi was a widow who lost her husband when her children were young. When her famous son was of high school age, she expected him to work part-time after school to help pay for the bills and groceries. Saroyan was very faithful and conscientious each week in giving his mother his earnings, but one week he spent all his wages on a record player. When Saroyan's mother came home that night from her job and asked her son for his pay, he explained that he had spent it on a victrola. Takoohi was livid with anger, so irate that she reached for a rolling pin to punish her son. Out of the back door ran the disobedient son, and out of the house ran the outraged mother to teach her son a lesson he would never forget. When she came out the back door, he came in the front door. Then she came in the front door, and he raced out the back door. This chase went on for several rounds until a brilliant idea crossed Saroyan's mind. When his mother left the house and he entered it, he turned on the record player and played music that filled the air. As his mother once again came through the door with the rolling pin in her hand, she suddenly stopped, charmed and be-witched. The haunting music pierced her heart and melted her anger. When Saroyan realized the chase was over and saw his mother in awe at the beauty of the music resounding in her home, he too stepped in the door. Takoohi put down the rolling pin, her anger turning to laughter as she said to her daredevil son, 'Thank God you are not a business man!'"

"What a story!" commented Mark, Michael and Anna's second son. "Again the humor originates in the interaction within the home. Actually I can easily see many of our relatives in the role of Takoohi Saroyan or Mr. Ara. But there's another hilarious Saroyan story that could just as naturally have occurred in our family. I read it in a newspaper that had a section of the feature page devoted to a column entitled 'The Best Advice I Ever Received.' Saroyan was asked this question, and this is the story he told. He knew he wanted to be a writer, and he had great aspirations to become famous. He convinced himself that to be an eminent writer he needed to associate with artists and live for a year in Paris by the West Bank. Of course he did not have the savings to accomplish this dream, but he felt that one of his affluent uncles would gladly donate the money or lend it to him. So he wrote an enthusiastic letter filled with hope that described his great ambition and waited confidently for his uncle's favorable reply. After all, Uncle Khosrov had the money and Bill Saroyan was a favorite nephew. At long last the telegram arrived. When Saroyan opened the letter, all he saw were three words. He read and re-read the puzzling words which at first did not make sense to him: 'HAVE HEAD EXAMINED.' What in the world did his uncle mean? Then it dawned on him. The answer was NO. Disappointed and crestfallen, Saroyan could not understand why his generous and loving uncle would refuse such a natural request. As he pondered his uncle's words, Saroyan realized that his uncle was no fool. The grandiose idea of going to Paris was nonsense. A writer with talent needs no such perquisites. Saroyan needed no special background, atmosphere, or association to prove his ability as a writer. Either he had the talent or he didn't, and a gifted writer can write anyplace. Uncle was absolutely right, and Saroyan said that those three words—HAVE HEAD EXAMINED—were the best advice he ever received. Yes, it brought him down to earth where he belonged."

"If we keep this up, we'll go all night," Stepan interrupted. "Such delightful stories! Such robust humor! But we'd better stop before everyone is yawning. Our discussions after the story have been as lively and fascinating as the stories. Chaucer would have approved and so would Cervantes. After all, the talk between Don Quixote and Sancho Panza was just as lively and surprising as their marvelous adventures. We'll wait and see what delicious fare we'll have tomorrow evening for our storytelling pleasure. Let's see. We'll shift from comedy to love stories tomorrow night. Let's hear how husbands and wives find each other, and also we want the children to know how some of their parents met and fell in love. These are always some of the best stories, but often they are not in wide circulation among the family members, not even in bits and pieces. "It's good for all you cousins to know how these things happen so that you're not too impulsive or too impatient. Your turn will come soon."

The day came and went quickly. The evening flew by, and everyone looked forward to another day of vacation and another night of stories and conversation. The cousins were beginning to sense how much they were learning, what a rich family history surrounded them, and how much affection and warmth surrounded them in their extended family of aunts and uncles and cousins. Whether or not they realized it, they were learning the meaning of culture—people enjoying each other's company, following a common way of life, inspired by the same ideals, constantly sharing their wisdom and knowledge, and always giving and receiving in the spirit of friendship and hospitality. Yes, all this human interaction was food for the human spirit and growth for the human heart.

CHAPTER SIX

Tuesday Night: From Europe to Cape Cod— In One Second!

It was Tomas's turn to tell a story, and so he began with a short introduction. He was going to tell the Bedrosian clan two separate stories, but they were so logically related that they comprised one story. He debated whether to call his tale "Hard-Simple Decisions," "Rational Whims," "Male Intuition," or "The Speech of the Holy Spirit." In any case every one anticipated a love story for Tuesday evening, and Tomas did not disappoint them.

"I once went to a dinner-dance at St. Gregory's Armenian Language School and Camp in East Falmouth, Massachusetts—a camp of the Armenian Catholic Mekhitarist order of Vienna. The purpose of the event was to raise funds for the upcoming camp season. At the end of the evening I introduced myself to the camp director, Father Luke Arakelian, complimenting him on the beauty of the camp grounds and mentioning to him in passing that I too directed a camp the previous summer. As we conversed about the camp directing, Father Luke became more interested in my background and directly asked me what I was doing this particular summer. As a college soccer coach whose season began in the fall, I told him I had no immediate plans. I had recently completed my first year of college coaching and recruiting and decided to spend the summer traveling and visiting my parents in Massachusetts. In fact, I had even made a deposit for a college-sponsored three-week tour of Europe. However, just last week I cancelled my reservation and

requested my deposit. No one could understand my decision. I
was sitting in the back yard of my parents' home reading a book
when I began to consider the prospect of three weeks in Europe.
Somehow I wasn't thrilled at the idea of traveling with an anonymous group of students and faculty. If I were to make this trip,
it would be with someone special like my wife and family. My
feelings and convictions were so strong on this point that the
following day I called and changed my plans with no other opportunities before me. I know that my decision seemed erratic,
but it wasn't irrational at all—as you will soon see.

"Now that I had changed my mind, the rest of the summer assumed a different shape. So when Father Luke asked about
my summer duties and commitments, all I could say was that I
was free and available. Consequently, he asked for my telephone
number and indicated he might call me to ask about my interest
in working for St. Gregory's Camp that summer. Frankly, I wasn't
thrilled at this possibility. After being a camp director the previous summer with all the trials and tribulations this job entails
from homesick campers to lazy counselors, I felt I needed a re-
prieve. Anyway, I said good-bye and drove to my parents' home,
never giving the idea of summer work at St. Gregory's a second
thought. After all, so many people who say they will call never
call.

"The dinner-dance I had attended was on a Saturday night.
On the following Monday morning I received a telephone call
from Father Luke's secretary: 'We would really like you to work
for us this summer. We are understaffed and need a lifeguard
and recreation director for the summer. Could you help us
out since you have the background and experience for the
position?' I wavered and hedged, groping for some feeble excuse. 'I'll need to be re-certified in order to qualify as lifeguard. I don't know how long that will take or even if a course
is available at this time,' I replied, hoping to find a way to
circumvent this obligation.

" 'Oh, that's all right' was the secretary's reply. 'Yes, do get
your certification and come as soon as you can. We can use you
whenever you come.'

And so one week after I whimsically traveled to St. Gregory's camp to attend a dance, I was a full-fledged member of the staff. I found myself spending the summer in a gloriously beautiful spot at Cape Cod, a summer paradise of firs and pine trees, ocean breezes and salt water. . . . it was also at St. Gregory's camp that I met my wife, a woman I also met on that fortuitous first night of the dinner-dance. Just think of all that I would have missed if I had gone to Europe!

"I thought about it and thought about it. After checking with the lifeguard at the local pool, I learned that I could easily be re-certified in a few days. Half hoping that obstacles would present themselves to frustrate my application for lifeguard credentials, I was somewhat disappointed at the quick efficiency of the whole procedure.

"Next I half-heartedly told myself that I did not have to accept this offer to join St. Gregory's staff; I was under no obligation, and I had made no promises; it was not a question of honor or principle. Knowing full well the demands of administering a camp seven days a week and the constant supervision of children the job required, I balked a little, realizing it would not be a restful, rejuvenating summer. I hadn't quite recovered from the previous summer.

"But then a stronger, more compelling, more authoritative voice began speaking to me, the voice of conscience or the words of my guardian angel: 'How can you, an able bodied, fully qualified man of twenty-nine years with no fixed plans for the summer turn down the genuine pleas of other people—a priest no less—and refuse to answer their need?' I had nothing to do for the rest of the summer. I had already rested and relaxed enough, nearly a month. I had done all the reading and visiting I wanted to do on a vacation. I knew I was being called to respond to someone's urgent need, and I knew it was wrong to refuse the gift of self. The stirring of the heart, the voice of conscience, and the words of a guardian angel made it clear enough what my choice should be.

"And so one week after I whimsically traveled to St. Gregory's camp to attend a dance, I was a full-fledged member of the staff. I found myself spending the summer in a gloriously beautiful spot at Cape Cod, a summer paradise of firs and pine trees, ocean breezes and salt water. From questioning whether I should even work one day at the camp, I came to spend ten summers at St. Gregory's. It became a home, a family, a vocation, and a vacation for me. And (now we are getting to the love story) it was also at St. Gregory's camp that I met my wife, a woman I also met on that fortuitous first night of the dinner-dance. Just think of all that I would have missed if I had gone to Europe!

"All these wonderful events occurred because I consented to be a lifeguard and responded to a camp in need of qualified help. I hesitated and wavered when the secretary called me when I should have jumped for joy at my miraculous good fortune. I thought I was going to Europe to acquire culture, but destiny directed my journey to an obscure Armenian camp nestled in the woods of Cape Cod. I thought the summer was all planned and predictable, but instead it was strange, whimsical, and adventurous—full of surprises and unexpected gifts. I thought I was doing someone a favor and being charitable, but I was the one who had the unrepayable debt and felt immense gratitude. And all I ever did was say 'yes'.

"Now on to the second part of the story, the one you've been waiting for. The first time I met my wife was at this dinner dance at St.Gregory's Camp. Remember that I had decided to say no to a trip to Europe for some seemingly inexplicable reason. As soon as I had purchased my ticket to the dance at the door, I looked across the room and noticed this stunningly attractive woman whom I admired from a distance; she was the first person I noticed as I walked in the building. I could not take my eyes off her as I gazed at every perfect feature of her loveliness in my contemplation of absolute Beauty itself. She was so elegantly, exquisitely dressed with such impeccable taste. I kept telling myself, 'Who is she? She must be married; she must be engaged; she must have a boyfriend.' How would I ever find out? How does one ask these things? As the evening continued, I noticed that no one in particular was keeping company with this ravishing beauty or asking her to dance. Except for some brief exchanges of conversation with one of the band members—a man in his thirties who shared a family resemblance with her (it was her brother I discovered), she sat at a table with a younger woman of sixteen or seventeen years old, obviously a friend.

"Feeling bolder than usual and sensing that I needed to take the plunge for better or for worse, I approached this unknown, mysterious woman to ask if she would dance with me. She accepted. During and after the dance I tried my best to spark some friendly conversation, introducing myself and asking her questions about where she lived, what she was doing for the summer. She responded to these overtures but in a perfunctory, uninterested, reserved manner. I asked her to dance several other times during the evening—one too many I guess because she apparently disappeared for a spell of about a half hour (she told me she was hiding in the bathroom to escape from me). Even though she danced with me each time I asked, our conversation did not lead to familiarity or friendliness. I did not feel on easier terms with her as the night progressed. She did not appear interested but acted aloof and standoffish; she gave no signs that she wanted me to pursue this relationship or call her. I learned her name and hometown but did not feel encouraged enough to ask her for a phone number or to mention the possibly of a date. She was not unfriendly or discourteous, but she was not friendly or winning either.

"The evening of the dinner-dance ended, and I drove home thinking about this unbelievably beautiful woman. I had never in my life been so powerfully and so instantly attracted to a woman as I was to Siran. Now I began to understand the phrase, "love's contemplative." All the way home during the two-hour drive all I did was think about her and re-live the whole evening. At night I dreamed about her, and the following day I recalled and contemplated her image over and over again. If she had just been a little bit friendlier! I instinctively sensed that rejection awaited me if I dared to call and ask for a date. So I didn't act, filing her image in the back of my mind and resigning myself to disappointment.

"Do you know the saying that goes 'if something is truly intended for you, it will come your way another time'? It came my way another time. Our paths briefly crossed again, if only for a moment. At another dance in the area, about forty-minutes from St. Gregory's camp where I was now working, she suddenly appeared with two other young women very late in the evening. It was between 10:30 and 11:00, and the dance ended at midnight. This was totally unexpected, and I did not even vaguely imagine I would ever see her again. Naturally, I was most interested in this second encounter.

"Oh, hi, Siran, do you remember me? I've been here since nine o'clock. I didn't see you. Did you just arrive, or have you been here all night?"

"Oh, hi," she answered. "I just arrived with two of my girlfriends. They picked me up an hour and a half later than planned; my girlfriend is always late but never this late. I know. It's nearly eleven. The dance ends soon, and we have just arrived."

"Guess what? I'm now working at St. Gregory's camp. After the dance where I saw you, I introduced myself to the director, Father Luke. He needed more help for the summer and asked if I would join the staff. So far I've been there about three weeks and am enjoying the summer at Cape Cod. How have you been? How is summer school going?"

"We danced a few times, conversed a little. Before we knew it the Armenian dance in Plymouth ended at midnight, and we went our separate ways. This chance meeting was a delightful surprise. I never expected to see Siran here and to meet her so soon. Nothing significant transpired to foster our relationship, except that we were quickly reminded of each other. She was neither more nor less friendly than she was during our first encounter. She seemed to remember and recognize me, yet she was not obviously overjoyed or overtly friendly. She had not taken note of me as someone special or memorable. I apparently was just another man at a dance. I still did not feel as if I had enough of a case or proper encouragement to call or develop a romance. She may have agreed to a date, but there was a strong likelihood she might have refused because I was still a stranger to her. I didn't feel inclined or moved to pursue the matter.

"The summer came to a close. It was late August, and St. Gregory's Camp was sponsoring another Armenian dance to conclude the season and raise funds. I wondered if Siran would be coming. Obviously she knew I was working there and would be present at the dance. Her brother played clarinet in the band hired to perform at this event—as was the case at the first dance—and so she was informed about the event. I hoped she would come and even felt certain I would not be disappointed.

"She came. This time there was a difference. She smiled

at me when she recognized me; she introduced to her family who also came for the event: her father and mother, her grandmother, an aunt and an uncle, and a younger brother. She was a bit more open and communicative in her conversation. She seemed to appreciate the attentions I paid to her when I asked her to dance. I even felt that the primary reason she came to the dance was to see me and to be seen in a different light. The change in her demeanor was slight but palpable, and I detected it as a favorable sign. Instead of remaining the distant stranger I was becoming an interesting man to her. She was paying me more attention this evening and looking in my direction more often. Subtly and almost imperceptibly a signal was given: in a half-revealed and half-concealed way she had come to see me and to give some slight indication that perhaps we could get beyond accidental meetings at dances. Later when I asked her if—after this third encounter and beginning friendship—she was hoping that I would call and ask her out, she answered coyly, 'I did and I didn't.'

"The following day I knew it was my turn to respond. It would have been insensitive and slothful not to have called Siran and made some attempt at courtship. I had only one reservation. In about two weeks I was about to leave Massachusetts for the Midwest to resume my coaching duties. Should I start a relationship and not be able to cultivate it on a weekly, steady, regular basis? Should I start something that was going to end abruptly in fourteen days? Wasn't I wasting my time and hers? These thoughts crossed my mind and posed as convenient excuses. I was being stupidly logical, falsely prudent, lazy, and unromantic. Besides, it seemed as if she had written a letter and communicated a message to me that deserved a reply. My heart and conscience were speaking to me. They dictated that any refusal to attend to the genuine call to love or to be moved by beauty or to respond to a gift or to a gesture of courtesy was dishonorable and hardhearted.

"So I called a few days later and asked Siran if she would like to go out for dinner and then to a nightclub that featured Armenian and Greek dancing. She accepted, not warmly or enthusiastically but in the same quiet and rather unemotional tone of voice that was neither friendly nor unfriendly. I thought she was being merely courteous rather than genuinely happy to hear from me. No obvious warmth or joy accompanied her telephone conversation. 'Does she really want to go out with me, or is she simply unable to think of some clever excuse to extricate herself?' I wondered. But I also realized that there was a certain old-world Armenian modesty about her entire demeanor.

"The line was crossed. I had called her, I had revealed my feelings, and now I was going to be at her home in a few days. It had taken eight weeks to bring matters to this pass, and the prospect suggested little chance of success or fruition. Something seemed to be blossoming, yet the season was coming to an end, not allowing for the full ripening of the seed. 'Nothing ventured, nothing gained,' I told myself on the one hand. 'Is it worth starting any serious relationship at this late date?' I pondered on the other hand. All things considered, however, I knew I was doing the right thing and was excited to know that I had a date with this beautiful woman who conquered me with a single glance. Despite the coming end of summer and the slow, unpromising start of our romance, I was still glad that something finally happened.

"When I arrived at Dover Street in Brockton, I learned from Siran that she been ill with a cold that whole day. She had even tried to call the camp and cancel our date. As good luck would have it, I had already left the camp and did not receive her news. When I arrived at her home, she explained that she had no real desire to go anyplace that evening because of illness (Yes, I know, I can hear you saying it: the very thought of going out with me made her sick!). Since I had already driven about three hours already that day, I did not mind the thought of spending the evening at her home and looked forward to an enjoyable evening of relaxation and conversation. Siran's mother, bless her heart, asked if I eaten dinner. No, I hadn't. We had planned to have dinner at a restaurant, but those plans were now changed. So I feasted on chicken, pilaf, and salad, glad to replenish myself after an exhausting day. Soon there was a knock on the door, and Uncle John and Aunt Frances and Grandma Ashodian arrived. A little while later the door knocked again, and I was introduced

to Uncle Jake, Aunt Mary, and Aunt Rose. In a few more minutes appeared Kegham and Valerie, Siran's recently married brother
and sister-in-law. It was a Saturday night, and all the local relatives
were gathering at Siran's parents' home for an *achkeet loos* party,
that is, to wish the recent bride and bridegroom good luck according to Armenian custom.

"I thought I had come to escort my date and spend the
evening exclusively with her, but matchmaking in Armenian circles
is a family affair. Her bad cold and the party at the house thrust
me into the midst of the clan. I was introduced to everyone and
mingled with all the relatives, but I hardly spoke to the woman I
had traveled miles to meet and that I had waited a whole summer
to see. She spent most of the evening in the kitchen helping her
mother serve and clean dishes, offering me occasional snatches
of five or ten minutes until the next call for help but no extended attention or interest. Yes, she was bashful, but there was
something exquisitely becoming about her Armenian quietness.
I had seen it often elsewhere, even in my own family, and recognized it as an attractive quality—not as cold reserve.

"I did not know what to think. Was her illness real or
feigned? I saw that it was a bona fide cold as her nose ran frequently and Kleenexes were constantly required. Yet I found it
strangely coincidental that she should get sick on our first date
and have to call the camp and cancel. Was I all that bad? (No
comments, please). It's a good thing I had already left camp before Siran called and the news never reached me. If I had received
that telephone call—after waiting all summer and hoping for the
right occasion—I would have interpreted it as a contrived excuse
or as bad manners and dismissed all thoughts of ever trying again.
Even though I was wrongheaded in my thinking, the mistake
would have been such an honest one, and I never would have
blamed myself for rash judgment. She said 'yes' over the telephone, but now it seemed she changed her mind and wanted to
say 'no' before it was too late. That's how I would have wrongfully
interpreted everything. So there I was with a houseful of warm-
hearted, affable, hospitable relatives who entertained me marvel-
ously as my date—voluntarily or involuntarily—seemed too preoc-

cupied with household matters to enjoy my company.

"As the evening came to a close, I wasn't sure what to say after I said good-night. Should I simply, out of chivalry, have asked her for a date for the following weekend right then and there, hoping that she would feel better and be rid of her cold in a few days? Or should I have said nothing about the matter and just let the affair resolve itself to an unfruitful conclusion? I wasn't really inspired to try again, given my lukewarm reception.

" 'At least be a gentleman,' I told myself. 'Give her one more chance. Even if nothing materializes or develops by way of romance, you'll be leaving for the Midwest and things will just naturally come to an end with no hard feelings. At least I won't hurt her feelings and can feel good that I tried again and gave her the benefit of the doubt. So as I left that night and said good-bye, I made myself say, 'Well, maybe we can go out sometime next weekend if you're feeling better.'

'All right, I'll see how I'm feeling,' she replied matter-of-factly. 'Good. I'll give you a call sometime in the middle of the week and see how everything is,' I answered, feeling indecisive about the whole matter. She seemed happy to hear me say that.

"As I drove home, I felt neither discouraged nor elated. It was an enjoyable evening of Armenian old-world hospitality as I feasted, talked, and relaxed to my heart's content. Siran's family all seemed to like me and had unofficially welcomed me into the clan. But my real reason for coming to Brockton seemed frustrated. As I considered the thought of my second chance for a date with Siran, my desire to telephone her was halfhearted, and I began to regard the possibility of a date as a kind of duty to salve my conscience and as a courteous way of ending a relationship on a gracious note.

"Monday, Tuesday, and Wednesday all came and went, and still I had not called; I just wasn't in the mood and was not highly motivated. Thursday arrived, and I felt compelled as a matter of honor and good manners to keep my promise. So I called on Thursday to inquire about Siran's health and to ask her about her availability for this weekend. She was more relaxed during this telephone conversation than the first time I called her and sounded much more poised now that her health had returned. Her voice conveyed more affability, and her responses to my questions were not limited to the bare minimum of words. Perhaps she regarded me no longer as just a stranger. She indicated gladness in hearting from me and in anticipating the upcoming weekend.

"This is how it all began. During that first date and the following two that we had before my departure, the secret of Siran slowly unveiled itself; the real person came forth slowly, by degrees, just like a flower opening itself petal by petal and pronouncing the glory of its beauty. On the basis of those three dates, we corresponded until Christmas when our courtship was rekindled. Then we corresponded until Easter when we resumed our romance. On Easter Sunday I asked Siran to go with me to the Holy Cross Armenian Church where Father Luke, the camp director, was pastor and then have dinner with my family—her first introduction to the Bedrosians. In late afternoon we decided to visit her family in Brockton and join them for Easter. On the way to Brockton Siran suggested stopping at Field's Park. There on that beautiful spring evening as we walked hand in hand, the Holy Spirit breathed into me. My heart was burning within me, and I proposed to her right then and there. It was completely unplanned and unrehearsed on my part. I can only explain it as the power of the Holy Spirit."

"I love that story," responded Melanie's twenty-year-old niece Tamar, "especially that part on being a gentleman and acting chivalrous. I don't think men understand how very important that is to a woman. Just think. What if you did not do the civil, courteous thing of keeping your word and calling again? This whole romance and marriage would never have taken place. I also like the fact that you took the initiative and showed wonderful patience, giving a woman every chance to be herself and to know the state of her heart. We are very deliberate and don't quickly or easily fall in love with just anyone who looks handsome or happens to take an interest in us. We like to be courted, we want a man to win our heart, we need foolproof evidence that a man *really* loves us rather than just says he loves us. Let's say a man must conquer us. You know what I mean? Overcomes our reluctance, banishes our doubts, changes our mind—not by arguing with us or being aggressive or forceful but by loving us steadily in an honest, sincere, heartfelt manner that is unmistakable to a woman. Aunt Siran, you've been very quiet. Tell us what finally convinced you to say yes when you seemed to be in doubt and hesitate?"

"Tomas told the story well, but he left out some important details. First, the night I met him at the dance he was wearing a green suit. I couldn't stand the color on him; it had no 'pizzazz' and did nothing for his appearance. First impressions count, and that was not a striking first impression. Second, his haircut was too short, almost a military shave—not quite—but too short to suit me at a time when longer hair for men was in style. Also I had never seen him at any of the Armenian social events and dances in the area. To me he was just an odd stranger, perhaps someone just off the boat. Also after he introduced himself and told me some things about his background, such as his coaching of soccer on the college level, I realized he was much older than I was. He was twenty-nine and I was twenty. So why should I be friendly and encouraging when I didn't feel any keen interest? But I confess that the second and third time we met, he seemed less objectionable. His friendly personality and sincere ways put my first impressions in the background.

"I had told myself that the kind of man I wanted to marry had to have the following qualifications: I wanted to marry someone Armenian, someone intelligent, someone trim and athletic, someone who was more or less a homebody rather than a gadabout, someone religious, moral, and decent, and someone within four or five years of my age. The more I came to know Tomas, the more I realized that he fit all of my requirements except for the age factor, and that slowly disappeared as a major consideration. We joke about it: I was mature for my age and he was young at heart. Tomas read somewhere that, according to proverbial wisdom, a woman should be half a man's age plus 7. We fit the formula. Also let me say that shortly after my twentieth birthday, I began to long to meet someone who would be

perfect for me in marriage and prayed fervently and passionately
for this wish to be answered. The more I came to know this stranger
with the green suit, the more I realized that he was the answer to
my prayer. As I said, he had all the qualities I was looking for—so
many of them that the age difference became minor. Tomas did
not tell you that I did not accept his proposal in the park in
April until the middle of August. Yes, we women are deliberate,
and we need to be sure of this great step in our lives. How did I
become sure? Here's how: I hated seeing Tomas leave after we had
spent the day together. I enjoyed being with him so much during
the day and then day after day when he was in Massachusetts
during the summer that I couldn't stand the thought of saying
good-night. I hated being separated from him—even for a few
hours until the next day. How does one solve this problem of
good-night, good-bye, and separation? There's only one way: I
have to marry him. Do you see how practical and sensible we
women are?"

Anahid and Dickran's twenty-five-year-old son Gregory
liked the part of the story when his uncle mentioned the saying
that "if something is intended for you, it will come your way
more than once." He began, "It's good that your paths crossed
three times rather than once. It gives you time to think and not
rush into things. In that way you don't have to plunge forward in
some kind of wild, desperate way without knowing what you're
doing. In the space between your meetings you have time to think
about the other person and hear what your own mind and heart
are telling you. When something wonderful comes your way again
and again, it's a telltale sign of God's will. Often you're not sure
of what God's will is, but this is one way of recognizing it. It
works almost like your conscience that tells you something not
once but again and again to wake you up and make you pay
attention."

Anahid and Dickran's nineteen-year-old daughter Lucy
was also moved by the story. "Just think. What if you went ahead
with your planned trip to Europe? You would not have met your
wife, and you would never have worked for Father Luke that summer. In all likelihood your paths might never have crossed. When

you announced your change of plans, I'm sure someone must have thought you were just whimsical or fickle. After all, how many people make a deposit for a trip and then change their minds for no apparently compelling reason. I wonder how you knew you were doing the right thing rather than just acting impulsively."

Tomas had no simple answer. "Of course it did not strike me as some great either-or decision with everything at stake. It's not as if 'two roads diverged in a wood,/ And I took the one less traveled by.' I was sitting in the back yard and thinking that the trip was in about three weeks, and I actually was not looking forward to it. I had no desire, no relish at all in thinking of going. Why? For the reason I mentioned earlier, which is a very good, logical reason. I did not want to go to Europe alone. After I called and cancelled my reservation, I had no regrets. I was at perfect peace, and I never thought about it again. You could say that if it was meant to be, it would come my way another time. That's the simple explanation. I just acted naturally."

Michael's wife Anna was also thinking of the decision-making process, commenting, "In the story, Tomas, I remember you said something like 'And all I said was yes.' I couldn't help thinking of the Annunciation. That is what the Blessed Mother said too: Yes. 'Be it done to me according to thy word.' That's a powerful word. You said 'Yes' to Father Luke (to God too) and look what happened: you met your wife and spent all those years at Cape Cod working at the camp. Siran said 'Yes' to you when you proposed, and now look at your beautiful family. I've heard Dickran say jokingly and seriously, 'All I did was ask one question and all I received is a one word answer of yes.' And all of a sudden there is a human family, a little kingdom! You must always say yes to the right things and to the voice of God."

"What the story especially illustrates for me," Michael added, "is the way God's grace works. Both Tomas and Siran co-operated with God's grace at every turn in the story. They could have said no so many times. Tomas could have said no to Father Luke, he could have said no to calling Siran, he could have said no to trying a second time, he could have said no to the Holy

Spirit when he was inspired to propose to her. Siran could have said no, he's a stranger; no, he's too old for me; no, he's leaving for the Midwest and there's no point; no, I don't want to leave New England and live in another part of the country. But every step along the way they took advantage of the opportunity, made an effort, took a chance, and left things in God's hands. That to me is the beauty of the story."

"I want to come back to the idea of acting like a gentleman and the act of chivalry," Tamar interjected. "If, Uncle, you had acted less than a gentleman, you would have lost your prize and gem. Because you were honorable and treated Aunt Siran like a lady, she bloomed and blossomed. You awakened the princess in her. She returned your love only after you were tested, as it were, and proved worthy. Too many college-age women give themselves to men who are in no way worthy, chivalrous, or honorable. They don't have to pass any tests, prove their sincerity, or be real men. So many women are just used today by men who haven't a clue about real manhood and the meaning of chivalry. Women need to have higher standards for men to win their love. That's one of the evils of the pill—men acting selfishly, not honorably. It kills the whole idea of romance and destroys the whole mystique of love."

"I have just one comment on the story," added Stepan, "and then I think we should end for the night before our storytelling turns into the tales of a thousand and one nights. That story to me was about courtship—slow, gradual, deliberate— the revelation of a secret in stages of unfolding. It was full of little surprises and unexpected turns—like Siran suggesting they take a walk in the park, never expecting a proposal to result from a stroll. Siran calling to cancel the date only to discover that my brother was already on his way. Siran having no interest in the guy and then falling madly in love. Tomas on his way to Europe and then on the road to Cape Cod instead. The story captures the mystery of love. This mystery is gone in our culture where people live together instead of courting and falling in love and promising faithfulness until death do us part. A great story. But just remember: this is just one of millions of beautiful love stories. It illustrates something you young people should never forget. Marriages are made in Heaven. Pray as your aunt did that God will send you the person He has chosen you to marry and you will recognize him or her as clearly as your aunt and uncle did."

"Yes, we'd better stop here, or no one will get to bed tonight," Melanie remarked. "Maybe some of us can continue this topic of love and marriage on the beach tomorrow if anyone is interested."

"Excellent idea, auntie," said Talene, the nineteen-year-old daughter of Michael and Anna. "I've been wanting to ask this question, and this story is the perfect occasion to raise the question. You as first generation Armenians have all married Armenians, and it's obvious how much you all have in common. But this cannot always be the case, especially with our generation who are clearly more Americanized than your generation. How much priority or importance should Armenians give to the custom of Armenians normally marrying other Armenians? Would you be disappointed if your children married non-Armenians?"

"Oh, Talene, what a question! Discussing that one will take a whole afternoon on the beach tomorrow. See you there and anyone else who is interested," Siran concluded.

CHAPTER SEVEN

WEdNESdAy AfTERNOON: WisdOM ON THE BEACH

*A*s the various members of the family gathered on the beach at West Okoboji Lake on Wednesday afternoon, naturally the first topic on the agenda was the question of whether or not Armenians should—as a matter of principle or conviction— seek to marry only other Armenians. Several of the cousins—Talene, Arpine, Mariam, Mark, Harry, and Gregory—and three of the adults were present when the debate began.

"Well, go ahead, Aunt Siran," Talene began, "we want to know what you think and why because in Uncle Tomas's story you had decided that one of the qualifications for your husband-to-be was that he be Armenian. Why did you feel so strongly about that?"

"First, let me say," Siran explained, "that I did not absolutely rule out marrying a non-Armenian. I knew I wanted to be married, be a wife and mother, and raise a large family. If it became obvious after a certain number of years that no Armenian man was interested in dating me or marrying me, then of course I would consider going out with non-Armenians whose character, personality, ideals, and religion were similar to my own. I did not want to miss out on the joys and blessings of marriage. But my first choice was to marry an Armenian. That was my ideal. But I also had a second choice if the first one did not materialize. Women are very realistic."

"But what was the driving force behind the first choice?" Mark asked. "Was it family pressure or expectation? Following custom or convention? Simply following the example of others in your generation who were marrying fellow Armenians?"

"Not exactly, Mark," Siran clarified. "Let's say I loved being Armenian and did not want to give up that part of myself. I loved our language, our cooking, our hospitality, our music, our sense of family, the Armenian Mass and liturgy, and our entire old-world culture. I wanted to embrace all of that and continue it, not give up some of it or compromise it just to get along harmoniously with someone who could not possibly understand or appreciate it as I did. That was one reason. I wanted to bring full-blooded Armenian children into the world so that our nationality and culture could continue. After the tragedy of the million and a half deaths in the genocide, Armenians must rise up from the ashes and continue our race. We have a great, noble heritage that we must perpetuate. Our history is filled with Christian martyrs who fought and died rather than convert to Islam or cease to be Armenian.

"I have plaque on my wall, a quotation from William Saroyan. Perhaps you have seen or read it: 'I should like to see any power of the world destroy this race, this small tribe of unimportant people . . . Go ahead, destroy Armenia. See if you can do it. Send them into the desert without bread and water. Burn their homes and churches. Then see if they will not laugh, sing, and pray again. For when two of them meet anywhere in the world, see if they will not create another Armenia.' That quotation captures the Armenian spirit. They refuse to be destroyed. They will die for their faith rather than give up being Armenian Christians. You know the story of St. Vartan Mamigonian fighting the Persians. Vastly outnumbered, the Armenians died for their faith rather than accept peace at the loss of their religion and culture. In other words, when you grow up Armenian and know this Armenian spirit, you feel so proud of your ancestors, history, and culture. You feel grateful and blessed to be Armenian, you want to pass that heritage down to the next generation. It's just harder to do this when your husband or wife is not Armenian."

"Let me add something here," Michael said. "I always felt

that no one except an Armenian woman would ever perfectly understand me or easily accept my parents with all their eccentric Armenian ways. How can you be involved in an Armenian church or participate in Armenian political affairs or send your children to an Armenian camp unless your spouse is entirely in agreement and sympathetic? It's hard—not impossible—to be your true Armenian self with someone who does not perfectly understand your motivation and appreciate your strong convictions. Here's something else to consider. I know it's something that has probably never crossed your mind. The person you marry should be friendly, pleasant, and appreciative of your parents—not someone who has nothing in common with them. Suppose your parents especially enjoy family functions and gatherings for all kinds of occasions—birthdays, anniversaries, baptisms, holidays—and your husband or wife is anti-social or doesn't really enjoy these occasions. Do you see the problem? Suppose you grow up Armenian and come to expect and appreciate all those marvelous dishes you see in an Armenian kitchen with ingredients like bulgur, lamb, garlic, lemon, and yogurt, but your spouse doesn't like to cook or has no taste for Middle-Eastern food. Do you see the problem? I realize these are not insurmountable problems, and many Armenians who have married outside their nationality have enjoyed beautiful, happy marriages. I'm not denying that. I'm just saying that there is a certain folk wisdom about 'marrying your own kind.' It simplifies many things. It's not a cure-all of course."

Melanie was also present at the beach and listening intently to her brother and sister-in-law. She thought of something that had not been mentioned yet. "Just, remember," she began, "that the fact that you are a man and woman in marriage is a profound difference in itself. My femaleness and my husband's maleness provide plenty of areas of disagreement and argument. Every marriage has them, and every couple has difficulties in marriage in one area or another—how to spend money, how to deal with relatives, how to discipline the children, where to spend the holidays, how to keep the romance in the marriage alive. Because one of you is a man and one of you is a woman by itself creates a world of difference. You don't need more and more differences creating more and more complications when the whole point of marriage is to be one. The more areas of agreement, the more things you share in common, the more you hold the same ideals and moral principles—the more harmonious the marriage. You don't want to be arguing about everything all the time! Marrying an Armenian with whom you are compatible can eliminate so many sources of stress."

"For instance," resumed Siran, "generally speaking, an overwhelming majority of Armenian couples in my generation just took for granted without any need for discussion or debate so many basic truths that were self-evident and indisputable: marriage is forever; divorce is unthinkable; children are a blessing, and the purpose of marriage is to be generous with life; mothers should stay at home with their children and not send them to daycare while they work; fathers are the primary breadwinners in a family and should not expect their wives to provide a secondary income; contraception and abortion are always wrong; children should take care of their parents in their old age; a home is a place for hospitality, a place to be shared with family and friends as often as possible; being a mother and homemaker is an honor and privilege, not a form of drudgery; marriage and family are of far greater importance than career, money, or self-fulfillment. If you agree on these basic moral issues and ideals—as most Armenians tend to do—then you greatly increase your chances of happiness in marriage. That's basically what Armenians mean when they encourage their young to marry other Armenians. The chances for agreement and compatibility are much greater."

"To get to the point," Siran remarked, "is it wrong for Armenians to marry non-Armenians? Of course not! Nobody is saying that. Can you marry someone who is not Armenian and have a happy life? Yes, we know many couples like that. Will you lose some of your heritage and find it harder to pass it down if you marry outside your nationality? More than likely yes. Should you strongly consider marrying an Armenian and make an effort to meet young men and women of your age and ethnic background? Absolutely! But you don't marry someone just because he is Armenian; it's not the blood or the genes but the character, heart, and soul of the person that matters. All I am saying is that there are plenty of attractive, intelligent, loving men and women of Armenian descent that ought to be considered when thinking about marriage. Is there something higher than nationality and ethnicity? Yes, God. God's will is higher than continuing a particular race or nation. Always marry for love, not for ethnicity. If I had to decide between a good Armenian match or a good non-Armenian match, I would pick an Armenian husband. If I had to decide between a mediocre Armenian whom I did not admire or respect and a noble, chivalrous non-Armenian, I would pick the non-Armenian. That's the best answer I can give you. There is no eleventh commandment that says, 'Thou shalt not marry anyone who is not Armenian.' "

"What you say may very well be true for you first generation Armenians, Aunt Siran," remarked Harry. "You tended to live in the same communities and neighborhoods in places like Watertown, Worcester, Detroit, and Fresno, but we are all scattered nowadays and find ourselves living in towns and cities where we may be the only Armenian family. We didn't absorb the culture and live fully in it as you did, and so the thought of meeting and marrying an Armenian is very remote as I see it. Yes, we're Armenian on both sides of the family and know something about our background, but it hasn't been as formative as yours. All your reasons for Armenians marrying other Armenians make good practical common sense, but in this day and age we are more Americanized than you were, and so it would be easier for us to adjust to a non-Armenian family. In any case, I don't think it's as essential as you make it sound."

"I also think," said Arpine, "that, first and foremost, it's important to marry a good person who will love me and be faithful. That to me is more important than the fact that he is Armenian. If he happens to be Armenian too, that would be nice, but I can't say that I weigh that factor so heavily. Besides, I've met many Armenians who are Armenian in name only, and I have less in common with them than with some of my other friends. In the summer program I attended in Washington, D.C., with other Armenian students from all over the country, I found a whole range of backgrounds and attitudes from the conservative to the liberal, from the pro-choice crowd to the pro-life group, from those whose Armenian home life was like ours to those whose home life was thoroughly secular and materialistic. I'll just have to wait and see."

"Of course there is no perfect answer to Talene's question," admitted Melanie. "As parents all we can do is encourage our children to attend Armenian functions and events. We can ask them to try, to make an effort and show some initiative, and to give the thought of marrying another Armenian a real priority, letting them know how much it would please us as parents. We as parents must pray for this to happen and tell our sons and daughters that we know a wonderful young man or beautiful daughter that we would like them to meet. There is nothing wrong with matchmaking if it's done in the right spirit. There's nothing wrong with getting families together for parties so this might happen. We all need help in this area of matchmaking. That's all we can do. Whatever happens we must accept as God's will—not my will but Thy will be done."

"Thanks, Aunt Siran, for being so honest with us," Mariam said after listening intently to everyone else's comments. "It's so good to have adults discuss this topic with us in a calm, rational, thorough way without being rushed."

"Yes," Talene agreed, "and for answering our hard questions in a credible and wise way. It's so obvious that you speak with the knowledge of experience and with a heart of love. You don't give us pat formulas or stupid answers. You really make us think, and you raise points that I never even considered such as all the things husbands and wives have to argue about and how important it is to marry someone who will not create tension between you and your parents."

"That was the good thing in hearing you all talk on this

subject," Mark interjected. "Perhaps you didn't absolutely convince us, but you really gave us something to think about in this
delicate area of marriage where so much prudence and caution
are needed—where divorce is so easy. So many of my friends at
college have suffered the separation of their parents, and it tears
them apart. They see no reason for it, and they are the victims.
They love both of their parents and can't understand why they
can't be one family. Some of them say they don't want to get
married because of the probability of divorce and all the cruelty
that inflicts on so many people. What you are all saying is that
marriage isn't just passions or feelings but also good judgment,
common sense, and a shared faith—recognizing all the things a
couple needs to hold in common for real oneness. Having a
similar culture, tradition, religion, and way of life has to unify a
couple and be a preventative against divorce.

"Well, that is the point," Michael added. "The more knowledge you have, the more informed you are, the more facts before
you—then you can see the whole picture and make the best decision. As older people and as parents we offer you our knowledge
and experience on what works and what doesn't work. We've given
you the seeds of thought. And you'll be surprised how these seeds
ripen and bear fruit. A year or two from now you might be
thanking us for daring to tell you the hard truths that no one else
even mentions. The wisdom we offer has been time-tested. There's
something to it. It works."

"Let's go for a canoe ride and a swim before dinner,"
Greg suggested. The discussion ended on a note of deep confidence and genuine respect—the children sensing how the elders
cared for their future happiness and offered them their choicest
wisdom and the adults appreciating how intently the offspring
listened and wanted to know the truth. There was no real generation gap but real exchange, honest feelings, and hearts speaking to
hearts.

CHAPTER EIGHT

Wednesday Night: A Boy's Dream Comes True

As everyone gathered once again for the evening's entertainment of storytelling, Stepan thought he would give his audience a choice. "Let's see," he began, "so far we have been feasted with tragedy, history, biography, comedy, and romance. What are we in the mood for? I know we have some more comic tales in store and some stories about miracles and more Grandpa Nubar adventures. Does anyone have a preference for tonight?

"I do," said Aram. "I'd like to hear some more Grandpa Nubar stories. Those stories about the rubbers and the witches are out of this world. There must be more of those."

"There are plenty of those," said Stepan. "I'll tell you two of my favorites, one that will make you laugh and one that will move you. The first one I'm entitling 'A Boy's Dream Comes True.' It happened when I was eleven years old and began going to my first gym class.

"My love for basketball began in the fifth grade when, on Tuesdays and Fridays, we walked from Park Elementary School to nearby Milford High School for our weekly physical education classes. Like many other boyish activities, basketball soon occupied and absorbed all my free moments. After-school hours, weekends, vacations meant basketball, basketball, basketball wherever I could find a place to play. There's nothing I enjoyed more than seeing my shots go through the net.

"It soon became apparent that my enthusiasm for this

sport could not be gratified by two days of physical education activity each week during school hours. In those days in the 1950's in Milford, Massachusetts, there were no 'open' gyms where the basketball courts in the public schools were available to the general public for recreation. There were only two indoor gyms with basketball courts in the whole town, a town of 15,000: one at the armory where St. Mary's High School practiced and the other at Milford High School where my physical education classes were held. So how does an eleven-year-old boy with a passion for basketball play the game in the winter, the natural season for the sport, when there are no available courts in town?

"He learns to play basketball outdoors—in snow, wind, cold, and all kinds of weather. I recall whole Christmas vacations that we spent outdoors playing basketball on snow-covered roads that we shoveled to make dribbling possible. We dressed warmly in bulky coats or sweaters and other winter gear, accepting these inconveniences without any major complaints. We learned to shoot with a glove on our hand, or we took the glove off our shooting hand and played with one warm hand and one cold hand.

"Our basketball court was across the street, the backboard riveted to a telephone pole. In fact, it was the only basketball court connected to a telephone pole in the whole town of Milford. My father explained to me that it was against the town laws to attach anything to telephone poles. However, the law had to be bent and an exception made in our case. It so happened that a few years ago my father had given the telephone company special permission to place a pole in our back yard; there it was, a towering telephone pole, standing erect in our back yard in a corner by the garden. Apparently, the telephone company saved a lot of money and eliminated some major construction because Grandpa Nubar allowed them to place the pole in our yard. My father received no money for this favor but acted out of good will.

"However, Grandpa loved his children and wanted them to have fun. He liked coming home and seeing me and friends having exciting basketball games across the street. My complaints that we had no indoor courts for play and no outdoor sites to erect our own court set his practical mind to do some hard thinking. He decided that, with his permission and blessing, we could go ahead and use the telephone pole for a place on which to hang our backboard. If the telephone company protested, complained, called the police, or took the backboard down, he would remind the telephone company of the special privilege he granted them of planting a telephone pole in his back yard. If New England Bell refused to allow one of their poles to be used as a pillar for an outdoor basketball court for the sheer enjoyment of youngsters who had no place to play basketball in the winter, then the telephone company would have to remove their pole from our yard. Dad made his point very clearly.

"Although an appeal on behalf of the children would have had no influence on the policies of the telephone company, practical economic sense dictated that New England Bell make an exception in this case. Grandpa's strategy worked. He often used to say that in this world we had to be "as wise as serpents as well as gentle as doves." Many ignore that part of the Lord's teaching and forget that He expects us to think and be prudent as well as trust in God. We have to be as smart as our enemies and outwit them at their own game. He was very good at that; he knew how to play his cards and was a great poker player. Well, he had an ace in the hole, and he knew it. I can't believe how seriously he took this matter of our outdoor basketball court. So many parents would have just ignored their children or just agreed with the letter of the law but not feisty Grandpa. The telephone company, knowing that Dad meant business, dropped the subject.

"That was the legal aspect of our basketball adventure. After that was settled, there came another obstacle—the physical labor of building the backboard, lifting and holding the backboard and basketball hoop in place, and then riveting it into the telephone pole. How was my father to accomplish all of this by himself, I wondered. During this time of my love for basketball our family rented the first floor of our house to Fred and Eva Powers, a young, friendly married couple with two young children. Fred was in the plumbing business with his father and owned a pickup truck. Also Fred had played basketball in high school

Our basketball court was across the street, the backboard riveted to a telephone pole. In fact, it was the only basketball court connected to a telephone pole in the whole town of Milford. My father explained to me that it was against the town laws to attach anything to telephone poles. However, the law had to be bent and an exception made in our case. It so happened that a few years ago my father had given the telephone company special permission to place a pole in our back yard; there it was, a towering telephone pole, standing erect in our back yard in a corner by the garden. Apparently, the telephone company saved a lot of money and eliminated some major construction because Grandpa Nubar allowed them to place the pole in our yard and enjoyed the sport as much as my friends and I did.

"You could tell that, even though he was an adult, he never lost his boyish sense of fun. If we were playing outdoors when he arrived home from work, he always joined us in playing catch or throwing a football. It was only natural to ask him about attaching our backboard to the telephone pole.

"It was all very simple to him: he owned a truck, he possessed all the tools, and had the desire himself to shoot baskets after work. He gladly volunteered his truck and assistance when he saw my father building the backboard with solid wood. Only one last detail remained: buying the basketball hoop and net, the most enjoyable job of all. The great day finally arrived. When all was ready, Fred drove his truck beside the telephone pole with my father, brothers, and me on board to help hold the backboard in place as he drove it into the wood.

"A new era had begun in our lives! Basketball all winter! Basketball right outside our own front yard! It all came about so suddenly that it seemed as if one of those magical wishes in children's books had come true for me. It all began with my love of play and my special fondness for the game of basketball. Before I knew it, the whole world seemed to be in tune with my most ardent dreams. That basketball court, crude and homespun as it was, provided more fun for more boys than anyone ever imagined. It stood intact for more than ten years. The wood somehow never seemed to rot, and the bolts never loosened. Returning home from college to Metcalf Avenue in Milford in my 20's, I could always see my home-made, improvised basketball court and relish all the happy memories of fun-loving boys having some of the best times of their life.

"Our basketball court survived another test. When it was ready for use, there were no homes across the street near the telephone pole. Metcalf Orchard owned all the property. After the orchard was sold a number of years later to developers and homes were built on the land, one of the new homes was constructed bordering on our court. The occupants disliked the idea of a basketball constantly rolling on their hallowed lawn and a neighborhood of energetic boys yelling and cheering near their property. These new owners did everything in their power and through their mighty influence to remove the backboard and get rid of the neighborhood kids, but our basketball court endured. Soon Mrs. Cavelleti realized that her threat, "Go home and stay out of my yard, or I'm going to call the police," simply didn't work. If the telephone company dared to call my father and report that they were receiving complaints, he would merely threaten to take out the telephone pole that the New England Bell Company had placed in our yard. End of discussion!

"So neither the police, town officials, a big business, or rich neighbors could touch our beloved basketball court. Luck was with us all the way, and my father was the greatest man and best father in the whole world."

"Oh, that's hilarious," said Aram. "Grandpa really had backbone. No one was going to bully or intimidate him or throw the book of rules and regulations at him. He stood his ground. He was fearless, wasn't he? It's like the time he told the doctor to take his lock and get out of the locksmith shop and never come again. When he knew he was right, even city hall couldn't contend with him. It's amazing how combative and angry he could get he if he had cause. He did the city and the telephone company a big favor, and all he asked was a small favor for the sake of youngsters, and they were ready to make a big deal out of the whole thing. Somehow people forget that, first and foremost, you have to be human before you get technical and legalistic. Good for Grandpa! He brought everyone down-to-earth."

"What struck me about that story," remarked Vahan, "is the way you had fun in those days. You mentioned the boys in the neighborhood getting together after school and on vacations and creating their own fun and using their own imagination. The whole idea of the basketball court and winter basketball in the snow was your boyish idea, Uncle Stepan. You didn't depend on organized athletics, park and recreation departments, and volunteer coaches to schedule your fun. It came from your own spirit and creativity. You seemed to be always outdoors, even in winter, playing basketball in the cold. What a contrast from so many of today's children who sit in the house watching hours of mindless television programs and playing Nintendo games or passing time with the computer. You and your friends at least had a sense of adventure and daring, what used to be called 'pluck.'"

"Let me say," added Michael, "that the word 'bored' did not exist in our vocabulary, and I'm not exaggerating. We always had something to do, and we were very resourceful. Here's a typical summer day for the Bedrosian boys: from 9:00 o'clock to noon meet at the town park for a baseball game with all the boys in the neighborhood; after lunch we would go swimming at the town pool or play Monopoly or chess at one of the boy's homes; in the evenings we would play stickball on the street until it became dark, and then we would play kick-the-can until our parents called us in for the night. We did not need adults to organize or supervise any of these activities. We learned to share baseball bats and gloves, we learned how to make and be friends, we learned to plan and organize, and we even learned how to settle arguments with our practice of throwing fingers and choosing either odds or evens. We knew our parents were busy and working and did not expect them to entertain us; we knew how to entertain ourselves and draw from our own playful imaginations. Now that's a real childhood! And that's the secret of having fond memories!

"Yes," Tomas remarked, "Grandpa Nubar and Grandma Elise let us be children. They always encouraged us to play and invite our friends to our home and even fed them lunch or dinner. They let us daydream, wonder, imagine, read, and enjoy our innocence, realizing that childhood was a special time in a person's life. They went out of their way to safeguard this innocence. They never burdened us with adult problems or financial anxieties. We had a real childhood and just reveled in play. Do you know that one of my favorite poems is A CHILD'S GARDEN OF VERSES? I never read it until I was in college taking a course in children's literature. What struck me about those poems is that the child is always playing. He plays outdoors at the ocean and indoors with his soldier men. He plays in the summer in the hayloft and in the winter making tracks in the snow as a great explorer. He plays with friends and cousins, and he plays by himself using his imagination. He plays a game of hide and seek with the sun as he greets the day, and he plays at night as he enters the Land of Nod dreaming of new adventures. The lines that summarize the spirit of Stevenson's book and that describe our childhood are these:

> Sing a song of seasons!
> Something bright in all!
> Flowers in the summer,
> Fires in the fall!

Every time I read those poems to my children, I remembered my own childhood and realized what happy memories I have just playing, having fun, and never worrying about anything. And it's true! You never really lose your childhood, no matter how old you are. Your children and grandchildren awaken it, and there you are going back in time as if it were just yesterday—not forty or fifty years ago—that you were the child. Stevenson says it beautifully:

> 'Time was,' the golden head
> Irrevocably said;
> But time which none can bind,
> While flowing fast away, leaves love behind.

Here we are in our forties and fifties wondering where the time went as we look older and grayer, and yet here we are telling these stories and recalling these fond memories as if they just happened. Something has been left behind, the deposit of love as Stevenson says."

"Look what happens when you are deprived of a real childhood," Melanie remarked. "You lack a spirit of adventure, you don't develop a love of life, you don't become playful and fun-loving, and you have no imagination. How do you come to enjoy your own children and give them a sense of fun if the child in you is dead? I can always tell whether my adult acquaintances have had happy or unhappy childhoods. Those with real childhoods know how to relax, be spontaneous, and improvise. They are not so grim and deadly serious. They invite you to their homes, they use their kitchens and entertain, they tell you to bring the *whole* family when they have social occasions. On the other hand, I have some friends who never invite friends to their homes, even for a cup of coffee; they never initiate social events or call and say 'I'm going to the beach with my kids. Would you or your children like to join us?' No spontaneity, no mirth, no spirit of adventure! You can tell they don't know what fun is because they probably never tasted it when they were children."

"Speaking as a father," Tomas added, "I was moved by that part in the story where Dad acted as if that basketball court was his primary business in life. He didn't just put it in the back of his mind as if it were trivial nonsense and then go on to the really important business of his life. He really went out of his way to make his children happy. He inconvenienced himself, complicated his life, entangled himself with city government, and no doubt angered some people. Why? Because he loved his children and their happiness was foremost in his mind. It's good for children to see that. It's a fantastic proof of how much their parents love them and will do for them. Do you see how much that wooden backboard now means to us? Mothers are always giving their children proofs of their special love for their children from cooking their favorite meals to organizing birthday parties to caring for them when they're sick, but fathers need to do these kinds of things too. When you're a child and you have a special longing—to go to a big-league baseball game, to go fishing, to go to the beach—and you beg and plead with your father, and he always makes excuses, then you know you're unimportant and don't matter as much as work and money do. That's the message. Any boy can figure that out. But I can honestly say that whenever I pleaded and begged (and I didn't do it often), Dad really listened and tried.

"Stepan," Tomas interrupted, "it wasn't just your dream that came true when you saw the basketball court ready for play. I had several dreams—things I really longed for—that seemed to magically appear. I remember the red wagon I saw displayed at Aubuchon Hardware. Oh, did I want to have that to play with!

'Daddy, can I have that red wagon?' I repeated throughout the next days. He could not afford it, but he gave me some hope. Dad played some mind of numbers game in Milford that many of the men in town enjoyed for their gambling pleasure. If he won, he would buy me the wagon. You guessed it. A few days after my pleading, Dad won a good sum of money by luckily picking the right number.I felt as happy as a king enjoying my new toy.

"Another time I was longing to go to Fenway Park and see a Red Sox baseball game. Ted Williams was my hero, and I listened to the Red Sox ball games on the radio every day, especially when they played the Yankees in their great rivalry. Dad didn't have a car, and he worked all week, Saturday, and a half-day on Sunday in his locksmith shop, so the prospect of going to a ball game looked impossible, but guess what? Although Dad couldn't take us to Fenway Park, his friend Guido could. A week after my petitions Dad let me know that Guido and Eli, an older Armenian bachelor who worked in Dad's store and loved us children, would be taking us to see a Red Sox game. This was magic! Another boy's prayer answered. And what an experience it was to be at Fenway Park! We sat in the left field grandstand and arrived early to see batting practice. About five minutes after finding our seats, Ted Williams yelled to me, 'Watch out, sonny, that ball is coming toward you.' I looked up and saw a baseball land a few rows in front of me. I was the only one near to it but rushed anyway to have this special souvenir. Talk about dreams coming true! My first big-league ball game, Ted Williams talking to me, and a baseball for a souvenir! How can I ever forget this wonderful memory," Tomas finished.

"Oh, and then there was the time we all went fishing for the first time," Michael interjected. That was my hobbyhorse. Somehow I had this notion that I wanted to go fishing. Maybe some of our friends were talking about it, and the whole idea captivated me. Dad was not a fisherman, and he never suggested the idea or offered to take us. But he sensed how much I wanted to go and how burning my desire was. Again there was the problem of not owning a car. Believe it or not, Dad and Eli together came up with a plan for a taxi to take us to Beaver Pond and bring us back (a rather expensive cab fare, if I recall) so that we could enjoy the art of angling. I still remember the day vividly. There was Mom packing sandwiches and preparing a lunch for hungry appetites as we waited for a taxi. Think about it. How many boys do you know who have a taxi pick them up and bring them back from a fishing trip? Leave it to Grandpa and Eli to come up with such originality."

"As I'm listening to these stories of dreams coming true, I can't help but think of how much parents will do for their children—the length to which they will go for the happiness of their children," Anahid said. "We do these things for our children because of the example of our parents. A few years Lucy was on a swim club and qualified for a special state tournament. The competition was four hours away, so we drove four hours for her to compete in two swimming events that lasted no more than five minutes! Eight hours of driving for five minutes of swimming! But that's what it takes to make dreams come true for children. They, then, will have this precedent and be motivated to do these things for their children. Who else but mothers and fathers will do these things?"

"Not to change the subject too abruptly," Anna interrupted, "but as I'm listening to all these anecdotes about prayers answered and wishes fulfilled, I can't help but think of St. Therese's idea of spiritual childhood. Stepan, Michael, and Tomas give examples of children expecting everything from their parents and approaching them with absolute confidence. If children's hopes and dreams come from their pure hearts, parents recognize this fact and do their best to fulfill them. St. Therese says we should expect "everything" from our Heavenly Father because He is the best of Fathers and that we can never ask too much of Him. We learn this great spiritual truth from our life with our parents as we approach them with all our desires and expect them to magically satisfy them. St. Therese says things like 'God cannot inspire unrealizable desires' or 'He would not inspire the longings I feel unless He wanted to grant them' or 'Never has he given me the desire for anything which He has not given me.' The asking and receiving between children and parents helps us to understand spiritual childhood—believing, trusting, and hoping in God's goodness with the same confidence of boys begging to go to Fenway Park or to go fishing. We learn the confidence of praying to God from the confidence of asking our parents. A few days ago someone referred to Michael Arlen's comment: 'There is nothing an Armenian father will not do for his children.' If we know that about our human father's love, it's a short step to understanding the meaning of the Lord's Prayer addressed to Our Father."

"Again, that's another reason we need to keep the child in us alive and actually have a real childhood," Siran responded. Our spiritual and prayer life depends upon it. How can we grasp anything about the love of God if we do not experience the love of a good mother and father?"

"I thought we were going to hear a second Grandpa Nubar story to night," recalled Mark. "Is there time, or should we postpone that one for tomorrow night?"

Uncle Stepan looked at his watch and noticed the late hour. "Let's wait until tomorrow night. You have heard the name Eli mentioned twice tonight as a good friend of Grandpa who worked in his shop. Their friendship is actually the subject of the next story, so let's take our time with it rather than listening to it sleepily. Does everyone agree?"

Everyone agreed.

CHAPTER NINE

Thursday Night: Old World Armenian Friendship

As Stepan promised, tonight's storytelling was a continuation of Wednesday's bill of fare. He decided to introduce Eli and then let Michael give his account of the honorable, enduring friendship between Nubar Bedrosian and Eli Hovagimian.

Stepan began, "The person in this story is a man we called 'Grandpa Eli' even though he was no blood relative. Our friends would joke with us and claim we had 'fake' relatives. In fact, he was known as an eccentric man. He always wore green sweaters, for example, never any other color. The whole eighteen years we knew him he wore green sweaters for three-fourths of the year. I can't picture him wearing anything else or any other color. He was a confirmed bachelor and was not liked by any of the female members of the family who often objected to his table manners. But he cherished Dad's friendship and loved us children. A lonely man, also a survivor of the genocide, he became attached to our family and more or less adopted us as grandchildren. He lived for us, taking us to ball games, fishing trips, and outings in Boston. He spent all of his money generously on us, treating us to the best of restaurants and buying us new clothes for school and new Schwin bicycles for Christmas. How did he become an adopted member of our family and acquire the title of Grandpa Eli? Uncle Michael will be the storyteller."

"Before I begin," Michael explained, "try to remember some famous stories about friendship—tales about David and

Jonathan, Orestes and Pylades, Damon and Phintias—and see if the bond between Grandpa Nubar and Grandpa Eli compares with these. If these names are unfamiliar to you, I'll explain at the end of the story.

"One day a gruff, outspoken, opinionated Armenian came to Grandpa Nubar's locksmith shop to have a key made and a lock repaired. As Eli watched Nubar go about his work, he began questioning the master locksmith's skill and expertise. In no uncertain terms Eli offered his opinion that Nubar was a mere amateur in the trade. He, supposedly, knew more about locks and keys than the locksmith himself and offered his free advice and honest criticism. Nubar had to suffer all this unwarranted 'chutzpah' from a rude stranger. If Grandpa was furious at Dr. Berry's haggling about prices, can you imagine his reaction to Eli's know-it-all attitude? Needless to say, this was not friendship at first sight. Nubar could care less if he ever saw Eli again or if Eli ever became a regular customer. So what if he was Armenian? But the strange thing is that Eli kept returning to the Milford Locksmith, almost on a weekly basis, but he came for social reasons rather than on business. As Eli became a regular weekly visitor, a friendship slowly developed. Soon they realized how much in common they shared.

"Both had emigrated from Turkey because of the atrocities of the genocide and suffered similar tragedies. Eli had no family in America or in Armenia, and of course Nubar lost his mother and sister in the march to the Syrian desert. They naturally felt a common bond not only because of their similar backgrounds but also because of their Armenian way of life. They both loved their families; they were both hard-working, honest men; they were both fearless and fiercely courageous men. You already know Grandpa's story of escape and his skirmishes with death. Eli too was made of the same mettle. Although living safely in America during the time of the genocide, he returned to Turkey and volunteered to join Antranig Pasha's forces in their guerrilla warfare against the Turkish forces at the time of the genocide. Grandpa too was a volunteer in World War II. He had wanted to join the armed forces in his late thirties so that his children could receive all the benefits of veterans, but he was deemed essential for civilian life because he was the only locksmith in a radius of twenty or so miles. So week after week as these two men became better acquainted, they came to admire and like each other more and more.

"One episode in particular sealed this friendship and made it a friendship forever. As a result of injury in the Quincy shipyards where Eli worked, he was out of a job. Either he was unable to collect anything because of accident or he received so little aid by way of unemployment compensation—I am not sure—but he was so desperate that he came to Grandpa and asked to borrow money for food and rent until he could return to work. If you knew Eli, you would know that the last thing on the face on the earth he would ever do is beg someone for money. Armenians simply don't do that, no matter how destitute they may be. They have too much honor and dignity to stoop to that level. The last thing that would ever enter their mind would be to go on welfare even if it were available. For all his gruffness, loudness, and eccentricities, Grandpa Nubar had a heart of gold. Of course he could not possibly say no to Eli. He himself knew all too well the hunger, poverty, and misery of the Armenian refugee. So for the next several months he gave Eli all the financial help he needed during his time of convalescence until Eli could return to work and repay him. Remember that these are honorable men. Honorable men never forget their debts of gratitude. They don't just return the money they borrowed; they show their thankfulness in a thousand ways over a whole lifetime. They know that some things are unrepayable debts, and they remember their indebtedness forever. You've all heard the saying that 'God will not be outdone in generosity.' Well, Armenians also will not be outdone in generosity either.

"Once Eli returned to work and began earning his weekly wages again, he not only paid back every cent he borrowed but also worked in Grandpa's shop after his full day of work in the shipyards. After returning to Milford about 5:00 p.m., he would come to the store and keep it open until eight or nine at night so Dad could increase his earnings. On his days off and on all his vacations and on every weekend for about twenty years he worked for Dad for free! Yes, I said free. He would not take one cent for his labor. I remember vividly the shoeshine stand that was in the locksmith shop. In those days people tipped when you gave them a shoeshine. Eli would not even keep the tips. He put every cent and dollar in the cash register. He could never be grateful enough to Grandpa Nubar for his loving-kindness and Christian charity in his moment of dire need, and so he dedicated the rest of his life to repaying his immense debt of gratitude. That's Armenian generosity!

"Keep in mind that Eli not only worked for Grandpa gratis but also spent a fortune on all of us. A lifelong bachelor as I mentioned, Eli attached himself to our family and showed a fatherly and grandfatherly tenderness towards us. Every Christmas he bought us expensive clothes and the best of toys; he was always unsparing when it was for us children. He took us to Franklin Park Zoo, amusement parks, ball games, and restaurants. All his savings were spent on us children, just as all his spare hours were given to working in Dad's store. Everyone always assumed that Eli was a hired man who worked for pay. Only the family knew the real story. Another heart of gold!

"Do some of you know Hans Andersen's story 'The Travelling Companion'? In that fairy tale a fellow by the name of poor John does a simple, kind deed. He sees rogues abusing the body of a dead man in a coffin because the dead man had not paid these men his debt. Poor John parts with his last dollars to appease these greedy men carrying their vengeance beyond the grave, and then he forgets his good deed, never expecting any reward. He loved goodness for its own sake and followed the example of the Good Samaritan. A good deed, though, is never lost or wasted. It's like a seed that is buried, but in due time it bears abundant fruit. Surprisingly, the dead man in his coffin comes alive and repays poor John with miraculous feats that enable him to marry a princess. In the way Andersen tells the story poor John's good deed is done in the dead of night and in the secrecy of darkness. It seems as if no one in the whole world would ever know of his generous act. It's like the proverb, 'Do

such awe at this great friendship that he gave his pardon and asked permission to join in this true, ideal friendship that he did not believe existed. It becomes clear that there is nothing that Nubar and Eli would not do for each other on the basis of their friendship."

"I read in one of the Armenian newspapers something that relates to the kind of generosity and goodness we see in this story," Harry remarked. "It was a story on Steve Mugar, millionaire and great benefactor to Armenian causes. He said that his whole philosophy of life and the secret of his financial success was summarized in a saying his mother taught him, a saying he always kept in his wallet: 'Do all the good you can, to every person you can, every time you can, everywhere you can.' It's like the phrase the priests impressed upon us : 'Meesht parik ereh' (Always do good)."

"Uncle Stepan several times used the phrase 'a heart of gold' in referring to Grandpa," Anahid mentioned. "I witnessed this heart of gold in a slightly different way that I will never forget. Grandma Elise kept urging him to evict the downstairs tenants because they were not paying their rent. They were not good parents. Their two children were always in the house, even on the most beautiful summer and fall days. Not once did we see the mother ever playing with the children in the backyard. Grandpa kept saying, 'Wait. Give them time.' This went on and on for months. My mother and I did not like this couple, and we wanted to them get out as quickly as possible, but Dad kept delaying and ignoring our complaints. I kept pressing him about this, and finally, quite upset and irritated at me for being so meddlesome and annoying about a matter that was his business, he said in his most stern and severe tone, 'What's the matter with you? If I kick them out, do you know what will happen? No, you don't! What will happen to those two children? Where are they going to go? Here at least they have a roof over their heads. Never mind about the parents. I know they're good-for-nothing, but I'm thinking about those kids.' I was speechless. Never did it enter into my head that this concern would be foremost in a landlord's mind or that it would influence my father's economic sense. I'm ashamed that I did not give him credit for his sensitivity and for having such a good heart—a heart of gold. After he said this, I never brought up the subject again. Dad knew what he was doing, and who was I, a mere sophomore (yes, a wise fool) questioning my father's conscience about matters of right and wrong that he understood more deeply than I could ever imagine. Naturally, because of his own background, Grandpa sympathized with the sufferings and cruelties inflicted upon children, and he always showed special compassion toward them. I was humbled by what he said; he really put me in my place. Good for him! I deserved it."

"Given the nightmares he suffered in Turkey and his life as an orphan during a major part of his youth," Michael speculated, "you wonder how he acquired such a sharp moral sense of right and wrong. Although Dad was a profoundly moral man, he never struck me as an overtly religious one. He certainly had a fear of God, an awesome respect for God and the things of God, but he wasn't a churchgoing type. My guess is that his Armenian Christian heritage, his mother's teaching and example, and the influence of the larger extended family all instilled in him the meaning of goodness, love, kindness, honesty, justice, and generosity. You learn these things so naturally in Armenian homes where it is taught and lived day after day by not just your parents but also by your grandparents, aunts and uncles, and the friends of your parents. There's all this reinforcement. I can still hear him, again in his sternest and most severe voice: 'Don't you ever lie. I hate lies.'

"As we grew older," Michael continued, "we were sometimes tempted to think we were smarter than our parents. Of course our parents weren't educated; they came from the old country; they didn't speak perfect, polished, grammatical English; they didn't perfectly understand American customs; and they seemed backward. But it didn't take long to be cured of such nonsense. Dad was never afraid to show his fatherly authority or prove to us he knew more than we ever could have guessed. Anahid's example is just one illustration. Children don't understand this until they become parents themselves, but parents by virtue of the sacrament of marriage receive special graces—call it infused wisdom if you will—that more than compensates for the lack of formal education. Our father and mother had all the essential knowledge for being good parents, raising decent children, and knowing the meaning of right and wrong. Our mother, for example, knew us so well that she knew what we were thinking and feeling without our saying a word. She always anticipated our needs before we even made a request. She had this uncanny ability to please. Where does one go to school to learn that? Now that we're older ourselves, we marvel at much they taught us without our even being fully aware of it.

"Speaking about anticipating our needs," Michael resumed, "I remember coming home from college for Christmas vacation. Because Dad didn't drive into Boston, it was often hard to figure out how to get transportation to the airport. I didn't want to inconvenience anyone or beg someone to give me a ride. Buses did not go from Milford to Logan Airport, and the cost of a taxi was prohibitive. There I am pondering how to get to the airport when a telephone rings. A cousin visiting from the Boston area calls to ask if I would like to go back with her family, spend the night, and be taken to the airport on Monday morning. How was all this arranged without my doing a thing? Grandma Elise was talking to her sister, my Aunt Alice. That's all I know. The rest just magically happened. Let's just call this wisdom the knowledge of the heart. We know our parents had an abundance of it, and we were too naive and inexperienced to figure out that there was such a thing or guess where it might come from. Yes, it comes from God, from grace, and from the Armenian way of life that passes this gift down from one generation to another."

"Another night has raced past us," Stepan intervened. "We're passing down all our wisdom, all our sayings, all our stories. So don't ever say we never taught you anything. By the time we're through, you're going to be very familiar with the real nature of things. And we want you to compare what you're hearing in these stories and conversations with what you learn in school and in American culture. Maybe on our final night you can answer that question and tell us, all right?"

The question piqued everyone's curiosity, and everyone agreed it would be a fitting topic for the final night of storytelling.

CHAPTER TEN

Friday Night: Miracles Do Not Speak to Us Halfway

Stepan had asked his sister Melanie to tell Thursday evening's story. He introduced it very briefly, knowing the story spoke for itself and needed no long preambles. He began, "As you hear Aunt Melanie's story, just keep in mind that miracles do not just occur in the Gospels or in the lifetime of Christ. They can happen in ordinary life to anyone, but it's important to believe in them. I won't say another word."

Melanie introduced the story: "This episode occurred in the second year of my marriage when I was twenty-three and pregnant with my first child. Armen had just finished reading a short story from a paperback I had purchased for him at a yard sale. The book was Paul Horgan's HUMBLE POWERS. After two years of courtship and a year of marriage, a wife has a pretty good idea of her husband's taste in reading. Touched profoundly by the power and meaning of one of the short stories in the collection, 'One Red Rose for Christmas,' he urged me to read the story: 'Please, Melanie, you have to read this story; you'll absolutely love it; I know you will,' he persisted. Naturally I wanted to know what it was that excited my husband so much that he insisted I read it. I read the short story and was captivated from beginning to end. Armen was right: it was one of the most beautiful, heartwarming stories I had ever read. I remember commenting to him right after I completed it, 'That story should be made into a movie.'

"This story was like some treasure or secret that only the

two of us seemed to know about. No one ever recommended this story to us; none of our high school or college literature courses ever introduced us to the work of Paul Horgan. We felt that the two of us had found some lost masterpiece of literature, a great treasure. I need to give you a brief outline of the story because it will help you understand the miracle that will come later.

"In the story Sister Mary Agnes (Mother Seraphim) grieves over the loss of her twin sister, also a nun, Sister St. Anne. Sister St. Anne died because of a mortal illness contracted after exposure to the cold when a fire broke out at the orphanage where she cared for the young. The fire was accidentally caused by a chronically wayward, disobedient girl, Katie—a child whom Mother Seraphim finds difficult to love and forgive. When, after the tragedy, the bishop in the story probingly asks Mother Seraphim, 'And yet you must struggle, must you not, daily, not to hate her?' Mother Seraphim confesses, 'it is hard' for her to show real charity or forgiveness to Katie under the circumstances. A year elapses since the fire and the death of Sister St. Anne. Mother Seraphim becomes depressed with sadness over the shocking death of her beloved sister.

"The only thing that could console her, she realizes, would be the assurance that her dear sister is now in Paradise with God. And so she prays to her sister in Heaven to comfort her in her great sorrow. This is her prayer. Let me read from the story:

'Send me something, Mouse. Send me a sign. If you do that, I will know that you are with Our Divine Lord, and I will rejoice . . . . Send me a red rose, and I will know, and I will be happy, and you can pray for me.'

"About a year later Katie, the delinquent girl who set the fire and indirectly caused the death of Sister St. Anne, brings a Christmas present to Mother Seraphim. As she unwraps the green paper, she discovers to her amazement a red rose. Suspicious that the girl stole the flower rather than purchased it, Mother Seraphim cross-examines the girl, grows furious with anger at the thought of the child stealing the rose and then lying to her, and finally forces Katie to go the flower shop with her to uncover the real truth behind the story of the rose.

"To Mother Seraphim's amazement the florist confirmed the truthfulness of Katie's story. Although the child did not buy the flower, neither did she steal it: the man in the florist shop gave the rose to Katie, as he says, because of 'Christmas spirit.' But why did Katie decide to bring Mother Seraphim, of all things, a rose? 'But something told me to pick a rose' is her only answer.

"The bishop, in whom Mother Seraphim has confided, learns of her secret prayers and God's answer to the nun's request for the sign of a red rose to assure her of her sister's happiness in Heaven. Profoundly moved himself, he reassures Mother Seraphim that the red rose is indeed a sign: 'But miracles do not speak to us halfway.' The bishop concluded, 'But how do we measure the divine. We do not. Is it not enough that no matter by what means, the immeasurable act of peace and charity may move your heart today, in spite of yourself, and perhaps forever? This will be quite enough of a miracle, my child, about which we shall say no more.'

"And so Armen and I just loved this inspiring story of God's mysterious ways of being truly present in daily life. Armen could not agree with me more: the story should be made into a movie. Little did we realize that the story would become even more real and concrete than a movie. We read the story in the summer of 1973, and in December the story became autobiographical drama rather than a movie.

"I was pregnant with our first child and expecting on December 21. Keep in mind this date, and remember that Horgan's story was entitled 'One Red Rose for Christmas.' My pregnancy proceeded in a normal way for the first and second trimesters, but then in November my blood pressure rose and soared. The doctors were alarmed as my blood pressure rose from 160 to 170 to 180 to 190. They feared many things: the retardation of the baby's growth, the dangers to my health, and the threat of death for both me and the baby. The gynecologists diagnosed my condition as toxemia, even though I did not have the typical symptoms of swelling, dizziness, headaches, or protein in the urine. The medical term was now changed to 'superimposed toxemia' or hypertension even though I am not a nervous person by nature.

Now I had to visit the doctor three times a week for blood pressure checkups. You can imagine my state of mind and all the fear and anxiety I was feeling. To be married just one year, to be expecting our first child—and then to have these terrifying threats thrust upon me! Finally the doctor ordered me to be hospitalized and have complete bed rest to combat the toxemia and control the blood pressure.

"I couldn't believe this. All my life I looked forward to being married and being a mother. I was so happy to be pregnant, and now here I was on a hospital sick bed being classified as a 'high risk' patient and not allowed even to get out of bed to go to the bathroom. Never in my twenty-three years did I ever spend time in a hospital, and now here I was worrying about my health, the baby, and all the dangers that threatened mother and child. Every hour or so a nurse came by to check my blood pressure as if my condition were an emergency. I couldn't stand it!

"This regimen went on for over a week, and all I could do the whole time was think, pray, hope, and worry. That's all. I so longed to bring forth a healthy baby not only for me and Armen but for mother and father and the whole family. With all the sadness in the lives of our parents I so longed to give them this joy of another grandchild. There had been recent miscarriages on both sides of the family during the past two years, and the last thing I wanted was to add to this sorrow. I knew the greatest happiness I could give our parents was the blessing of a grandchild. Armenians cherish life, family, grandchildren as the greatest treasures in life. '*Asee-eh giankee haroosdutiun*'(This is the real wealth of life) is a phrase I heard all through my life.

"All these thoughts keep crossing my mind as I wait and wait for the baby to grow to full term and delivery. My due date is about three weeks away. As I'm trying to glimpse the uncertainty of this trial, I suddenly remembered something. I remembered the story Armen and I had read during the summer, 'One Red Rose for Christmas,' and recalled the miracle of the sign of the rose. So far I had been praying for a healthy baby, for the healing of my toxemia, for a safe passage in the giving of birth, and for the happiness of giving my parents the joy of a grandchild. But now I decided to be even more precise and particular in my prayers. I decided to ask for a sign just as Mother Seraphim did in the story. So I added one more petition to my prayers: 'Oh, please, dear God, give me a sign that all will be well with me and the baby, a sign that will give me peace and keep me from worrying constantly and raising my blood pressure even more. O Lord, have Armen bring me something from one of his runs while he is jogging. He has never done this. I know this will be a sign from you that my prayers are answered. Please, please, Lord. I need this sign desperately. Lord, have mercy. Christ have mercy. Lord, have mercy.'

" 'Why not ask for a sign?' I thought. 'God is our Father, the best of Fathers. A father does not give stones when his children ask for bread nor scorpions when they ask for fish. His Sacred Heart is an ocean of mercy. What compassion God showed to Mother Seraphim in the story!' I knew this was a real test of my faith. So I prayed every day and many times during the day that Armen would bring me this specific sign—something he found on one of his daily runs for exercise. This was my most secret wish that I communicated to no one. Armen was not in the habit of bringing me anything from his jogging trails, not even a wildflower gleaned from a field. Besides, it was late November, and there were no flowers to pick anyway. So what could he bring if anything? I knew I was asking for a miracle.

"Armen visited me every day after work and spent the evening with me in the hospital. I knew his routine. He would finish work at about 4:00 p.m., go home and run for a half hour, and then come to the hospital from dinner time to 10:00 p.m. Of course Armen had no idea of my prayers for a sign, not a clue that I was thinking of Paul Horgan's story. Armen, why don't you tell the next part of the story?"

"All right," Armen agreed, "I'll continue. It was a Thursday afternoon, and I decided I would run my miles on the college track. As a completed a lap or two, I noticed a shiny silver object on the ground. Slackening my pace, I decided to look at it more closely. As I paused and peered, I recognized it was a coin, a quarter. 'Oh, well, just a quarter,' I said to myself. 'There's no point to picking up this coin as a good luck token. I'll leave it for some youngster to find. What's a quarter? It's not going to make me or break me.' But then another thought rushed into my mind: 'I know, I'll pick up this coin and bring it to Melanie as a form of good-luck.' So on the next lap I stopped and took the coin, holding it tightly in my hand as I finished my laps. I told myself to bring it to the hospital that night. 'It might lift her spirits a little,' I told myself, knowing that Melanie needed hope and cheer during this dark night of the soul.

"When I visited her that night, Melanie told me of the doctor's reports and tests. An amniocentesis had revealed that the baby's lungs were not adequately developed yet for a Caesarean section to be performed. A team of gynecologists wanted her to remain in complete bed rest until the baby's growth in the next week or so allowed this surgery. That was the plan of action—to remove the baby at the soonest possible moment to relieve the blood pressure. Melanie was angry, upset, and depressed at this news. I can hear the words and the tone of voice: 'What a waste of time!' she complained, referring to all the childbirth classes we had taken together in anticipation of giving birth naturally. Then she continued, 'I don't want to have major surgery; I don't want to undergo that long recuperation that follows that kind of operation.' She felt so disappointed that she could not experience the natural birth process and the consciousness of watching her child issue from the womb. We both felt so helpless. Nothing was happening the way we hoped and planned. What could I say to offer comfort and encouragement? All I could say was something like, ' I don't want you to have a Caesarean either. But what can we do? If it's the safest course for you and the baby, we have to do it, even though we'd rather have it the other way. Let's just keep praying and hoping. That's all we can do. I had been praying the Memorare constantly: 'Remember, O most gracious Virgin Mary, that never was it known that anyone who fled to thy protection, implored thy help, or sought thy intercession was left unaided . . . .' I'll stop here, Melanie. Go ahead and finish the story."

"Remember the quarter that Armen mentioned he found

on the track? The coin he was supposed to bring me as a good-luck token? Guess what? He brought it with him but totally forgot to give it to me! I desperately needed that sign after hearing all the news about major surgery, but it was not forthcoming that night when he actually had it in his pocket. That was on Thursday night. So here am I pleading for a sign, and there is Armen at home saying the Memorare each night. Armen came the next night, and again we sat and talked and talked from about 6:00 to 10:00. I mentioned all the calls I had received and showed him all the get-well cards that had been coming. I needed every moment of his presence to help me through this crisis, and all day long I looked forward to his visit. Ten o'clock had arrived, and Armen was about to say good-night and give me a good-bye kiss when he casually remarked, 'Oh, by the way, here's a good-luck quarter. I forgot to give this to you last night. Keep it as a reminder of hope and trust that all will turn out well.'

"You can imagine my reaction," Melanie continued. " 'Where did you get that?' I said in utter disbelief.

'I found it when I was jogging yesterday. Why? Why are you looking so strange and amazed?' Armen answered with complete innocence. 'You don't believe me?'

'Really? Oh, come on! Where on your run? You couldn't have actually found it! You never find things when you are jogging,' I said skeptically.

'At the college track. Why? What's the matter? Why do you look so surprised? I'm not making it up!' Armen insisted.

'Please, just tell me the truth. Did you *really* find it, or did you just take the quarter out of your pocket to cheer me up?' I persisted.

'I found it! On the track! Why? Why do you keep asking whether or not I found it and whether or not I am making up some tall tale? It's just a quarter, a little something to cheer you spirits. That's all,' Armen argued

'No, that's not all,' I replied. 'You're not going to believe this. I can't believe this either! Do you know what that quarter means? It means that the baby is going to be all right and that the baby and I are out of danger.'

'What do you mean?' Armen asked with a quizzical look.

'Do you remember the story you asked me to read last summer, the one about the red rose from the paperback I bought for you at a garage sale?' I reminded him.

'Sure, of course, I remember it. What about it?' Armen asked in total bewilderment at what I was trying to say.

'Well, I did just as the sister did. I prayed that I too—like Mother Seraphim—would be given a sign that the baby would be healthy and that I would be out of danger from high blood pressure. I prayed that you would bring me something from one of your runs if the baby was going to survive this ordeal. That's why I wanted to know for certain whether or not you actually found the quarter,' I explained.

'Oh, I found it all right,' Armen replied. 'There's no question about that. This is unbelievable!'

"We were both in awe. We knew we were experiencing a miracle. The God of heaven and earth had spoken, and we were speechless. Our hearts were on fire. We were so happy that we felt like crying. We did not once doubt the outcome after this revelation. All the anxiety, tension, and fear had dissipated. The message of the quarter was as perfectly clear to us as the gift of the rose was to Mother Seraphim. Do you remember the words of the bishop to Mother Seraphim? 'Miracles do not speak to us halfway.' How the baby was to be delivered—natural birth or C-section—was no longer of primary importance. We both felt rescued from all the dangers and complications that threatened the baby and me. What a deep peaceful joy we felt that night as our hearts were on fire. We were in wonder at the tender, personal, sensitive nature of God's love.

"So were we just imagining all this? Was it just wish-fulfillment, forcing our desires and hopes with false optimism into a situation whose hard facts we could not face? No, we weren't daydreaming or avoiding the truth. How could we doubt the providential, miraculous facts? God had answered my prayer. I received the sign I asked for. That's all I needed. The rest was secondary. All that remained was waiting.

"Remember that this episode with the quarter occurred

on Friday night. The following Thursday was scheduled for the
Caesarian-section birth. But on Monday night just before Armen
left at 10:00 p.m.–what unbelievable timing– my bag of waters
broke. I went into labor late that night and into the early morning and delivered a small but healthy four-pound, eleven-ounce
baby at 5:30 a.m. Let's say that God and Nature took my case
into their hands because it required a specialist."

"Aunt Melanie, do you have a copy of that story, 'One
Red Rose for Christmas'?" asked Michael's daughter Tamar. "I
have to read that story and remember it. I want to know the story
by heart and tell it to my own children and grandchildren. A
story like that makes you fall in love with life all over again. It
was absolutely beautiful."

"I didn't bring the book HUMBLE POWERS, and I don't
have a copy of "One Red Rose for Christmas' at hand. I won't
part with the book or lend it to anyone. I'll make a Xeroxed copy
and mail it to you and for anyone else who would like to read
Horgan's story in its entirety. That book and the quarter, which
is pasted in my son's baby book, are family heirlooms, holy relics
as it were," Melanie answered. "These miracles in our lives teach
us never to give up hope and make us realize that good can come
out of evil. You're right, Tamar, events like these renew us and
make the whole world look new and beautiful again."

"Try telling your story to the doctors," Tomas commented.
"I wonder what they would have said. Did you ever tell them all
the details or mention anything about the rose and the quarter?
I'm just curious."

"No, I never did," Melanie responded. "Somehow I didn't
feel they would understand or believe me. Of course they just
had to ask me–at twenty-three, mind you–if I desired a tubal
ligation. That question alone told me something about their attitude and philosophy that convinced me not to tell them the
story. I thought about telling them about how my prayer was
answered and how prophetic the sign of the quarter was, but
when I saw them for my post-partum checkup, the first question
they asked me was, 'What kind of contraception will you be using?' When we told them that we did not practice contraception

but instead would follow natural-family planning, the doctor gave us one of those strange, half-disgusted stares that said everything. No, there was no point in sharing the mystery of that birth with my team of gynecologists. They were scientists, and to them faith was not a form of knowledge. They would be skeptical about miracles or call them accidents.

"I had the sense that in their eyes drugs were the only medicine and men of science the only healers. They were good doctors in terms of handling my case and using good judgment. They delivered the baby with great skill and dealt with my high blood pressure in the best way they could. I am very grateful for their knowledge and professionalism. But they were sometimes very insensitive about the moral issues. They somehow are callous and blind when it comes to the delicate issues, thinking that because they are the absolute authority in medical procedures, they are also wise in moral questions as well. Not necessarily. In fact, one of the gynecologists strongly advised us not to have any more children because of my toxemia, arguing it was too great a risk."

"So what did you do, Aunt Melanie, after the doctor warned you against having more children," asked her niece Arpine. "You went on to have more children. What convinced you to do that after all the anguish you underwent to have the first baby?"

"Naturally we had to be prudent and sensible and weigh all things very deliberately and carefully," Melanie continued. "I took very seriously the gynecologist's advice to see an internal medicine specialist to determine if there was some problem with any of my major organs that was causing the high blood pressure. We were referred to Dr. McBride, and to this day we are so grateful that he was the physician who conducted the tests and gave his evaluation. Before any tests were taken, I remember sitting in his office and having a leisurely conversation with him about my whole pregnancy, about my family background, and about our great desire to have more children. It was soon evident that Dr. McBride was not merely a trained doctor who knew his medicine and was an authority on internal medicine but also a father of a large family and also a devout Catholic. He truly understood our situation, and we felt it easy to open our hearts to him along with just discussing the medical facts and test results. He prescribed a number of tests and scheduled another appointment for consultation.

"When all the test results were available, we met with him a second time, and he gave us the good news and offered his own human wisdom. The tests did not indicate any internal problems with major organs. All things considered—the medical facts of the first pregnancy, the results of the tests, and our deep desire to have a larger family—he did not see any strong, compelling reason for us not to have more children. He recognized, however, that I would be classified as 'high risk' and checked more frequently and carefully than the usual pregnant mother. I still remember his kind fatherly eyes and felt his Christian heart speaking as he uttered those words. This was our second opinion. The gynecologist and the internist gave us conflicting advice, but we both realized that Dr. McBride's words confirmed the desires of our heart. It was the chance we had to take."

"I give you credit, Aunt Melanie," said her niece Lucy. "Many women in your situation would have hesitated and not taken the risk. But then again you had just witnessed a miracle that had strengthened your faith and increased your confidence in God. These decisions must be so hard. I don't know what I would have done in your situation. I guess you just have to follow your heart."

"Both your head and your heart, Lucy," interjected Armen. "Both your mind and your feelings are involved in these decisions. You need good practical judgment and deep faith. You can't just say 'I want to have more children' and then ignore all the good advice and test results the doctors give you. That's rash and stupid. You can't just say "God will provide' and ignore common sense and hard facts. But then again you can't be so ruled by your head that your deepest feelings and desires are ignored. You can't be paralyzed by fear and caution. The head often calculates too much. This could happen, that could happen; this is dangerous, that is risky. You gather all the information available; you ask for the advice of wise people; you search your conscience; you weigh all these things; and you pray about it. In these kinds of situations you realize the truth of St. Ignatius's words: Act as if everything depended on you, and pray as if everything depended on God. You won't be left in a state of confusion or uncertainty. Despite all our confusion Melanie and I both never questioned our decision after we made it. Your conscience and heart will speak to you if you let it. You do have to believe in God's Divine Providence."

"You were saying earlier, Melanie, that Horgan's story should be made into a movie, but I think your story is just as classic as Horgan's," remarked Anna. "I kept thinking of all the parallels. In 'One Red Rose for Christmas' it was the naughty girl Katie who was the agent of God. The rose did not come from an angel but from this difficult child. She was the least likely candidate, the naughtiest girl, the one who set the fire, the one Mother Seraphim struggled to love, yet God's grace came through her. What a surprise! In your story, who knows, someone might have expected your prayer to be answered by uncle's finding a locket or a beautiful piece of jewelry—something beautifully romantic! But, no, it was a mere quarter—not a $100 bill—a dirty, grimy quarter stepped upon on the track. So how does God come into the world? Not as a mighty king or conquering general but as a baby. Through whom does He come into the world? Not as the offspring of a great royal family but from a lowly handmaiden. Remember how skeptical Mother Seraphim was just assuming that Katie stole the rose. Remember how suspicious Aunt Melanie was, saying 'Come on! Did you really find the quarter, or are you just making it up'? Remember again the dates: a red rose for Christmas in the story and a lucky quarter for Christmas in your life. Once again we see the God of Surprises using His unbelievable creativity and imagination as He interacts with ordinary people in their everyday lives. What an incredible way to understand and appreciate the meaning of grace! It comes to us in the most unexpected ways and in the most surprising appearances and in the midst of ordinary life."

"I know, I was thinking something like that too," added Harry. "You can study theology in a college course, but sometimes it gets so abstract or dry that it's hard to relate clearly to your own life. Sometimes I just get lost trying to understand theological vocabulary and terminology, especially if the instructor has no gift for connecting these theological points to human experience. The same with some courses in philosophy. Yes, the five proofs for the existence of God make perfect rational, logical sense, but often these proofs leave you cold and don't give you the sense of a living, dynamic, ever-present, absolutely real God who is here and now. I was saying to myself that the story about the lucky quarter ought to be called 'The Sixth Proof for the Existence of God,' meaning of course some undeniable miracle in your own life."

"It's a story I never tire of re-living or retelling," Melanie concluded. "Every time I think about it, I keep hearing Augustine's words: 'You love us, Lord, as if we were the only one.' As a mother I have come to appreciate that sentence even more. You love each of your children equally as if each one of them was your only child. You do not have a favorite son or daughter, but somehow they all feel special. They all adore you as their mother. They all feel that there is nothing you would not do for them, that they are the apple of your eye, that your love for them is most intimate and personal, that you know their hearts and understand them better than anyone else in the world, and that they are the center of your whole life. That's what every good mother or father wants to convey to children. But that's exactly how I felt as a result of the miracle. God loves me that much? Of all the things He has to do in this universe and of all the billions of lives He must care for, He is going to give my prayer first priority? He is going to stop everything else and take care of me? That's exactly what it seems like. But then again I am just one among millions that feels this way. So what kind of love is this that makes so many people from Augustine's day to my own time say, 'You love us, Lord, as if we were the only one.' You know you've touched a mystery when you ask a question like that. You've glimpsed something about divine love, about the infinite value of each soul, about the preciousness of each human being. That anyone, above all almighty God, could care that much about me just dazzles the mind. You begin to realize that, yes, the very hairs of our head are numbered."

As the evening ended, the nieces and nephews felt that they been brought to the heart of reality. This story was like an arrow that pierced to their very center, to the core of their being. God's love had melted their aunt, and now her heart had touched everyone else's heart. And to think that some of them moaned and groaned at the thought of spending evenings listening to stories instead of watching television or listening to popular music. Never did they guess that they would be receiving such a liberal education when they were on vacation. They began to discern the distinction between information, knowledge, and wisdom and realized that their older relatives were making them repositories of the treasures bequeathed to them.

CHAPTER ELEVEN

Saturday Night: The Luck of the Fool

As Saturday evening approached, everyone wondered what kind of tale was in store for them this evening. Surely no family had an unlimited supply of adventure stories, comedies, romances, and miracle plays. Perhaps they had reached the climax with Melanie's account of the rose and the quarter. Perhaps the stories that followed would be anti-climactic. But how could they be, given these passionate people who tasted life with gusto and thought about their lives so deeply? How could anyone beat that story for sheer human interest, drama, mystery, and surprise? Any family that hires a taxi to go fishing can never exhaust its supply of stories. A taxi to go fishing! Not to an opera, not to a prom or a ball but to go fishing! The cousins wished they could have seen the expression and reaction of the cab driver when he arrived to transport his passengers and saw all this fishing gear waiting for him on the curb. They would wait and see what other types of literature their dramatic lives and zany adventures would inspire.

Some of the cousins who imagined that their elders lived very conservative, staid, predictable lives of routine began to have some second thoughts. Judging from these stories, this older generation had experienced more than their offspring realized and had participated in life's fullness and variety more than their children ever believed. Hearing these stories made their parents, aunts, and uncles seem so human, so down-to-earth, so youthful, so universal. Somehow they didn't seem so eccentric. For all their moral, political, and economic conservatism, these relatives were adventuresome, daring people who took chances, who made bold decisions, who put their honor, principles, faith, or life on the line. They knew something about the art of living—how to appreciate the little things, how to endure the hardships, how to make wise decisions, and how to see the humor of a situation. They knew how to cry, how to laugh, how to love, and how to fight, and they weren't afraid of expressing their heartfelt feelings, strongest convictions, and their justified anger. They were more real than their children, nieces, and nephews ever guessed.

No matter how old fashioned or traditional the Bedrosians were, no one would ever accuse them of being dull, half-dead, apathetic, or slothful. The children could not help notice how vibrantly alive their parents became in the larger company of the extended family—how quickly they laughed, how easily they joked, how witty they were, how delightfully they teased each other, how intelligently they talked. Yes, they had to notice and admit it: these middle-aged folks were children at heart and had not lost touch with that part of their humanity. The world had not made them jaded, cynical, or bitter. How they relished telling and hearing these stories! How seriously interested they were in each other's lives! It was a delight for the young to see how much their aunts and uncles truly enjoyed each other's friendship, conversation, and presence. They could not deny it: the Bedrosian clan knew how to have a good time without lavish expenditures, exotic travel, or liquor galore. Be with each other, cook good food, help with the work, let the children play, tell stories, and be grateful to be alive.

The college-age nieces and nephews knew that this was becoming a lost art. For the most part all they saw at college was beer parties, loud music, and entire weekends watching sports on television or watching video after video. The entire week of vacation was quickly becoming a refreshing contrast and an introduction to the art of simplicity and to the meaning of good-old fashioned fun with all its vigor and innocence. The cousins were talking about these matters on the beach when Harry asked, 'I wonder what Uncle Michael's story will be tonight. What do you think, Mark and Aram? You must know your father's repertory by heart. What are his favorite stories that you've heard a hundred times?'

"I wouldn't be surprised if he told some story like Uncle Stepan's tale about the basketball court. He tells us over and over again how he was never bored as a boy, how he was always outdoors playing, how the neighborhood kids organized all the fun activities, and how you don't need television or video-cassette recorders to have a great time. That's my guess, but he always has some new stories too that you've never heard before. I won't second-guess him. I know he ran in the Boston Marathon and traveled to Europe once and has some tales about those adventures. I can't say. Remember: the Bedrosians can't be figured out! They will always throw you a pitch you haven't seen before."

"Take a guess. Will it be serious, comic, religious, or none of the above?" Harry asked.

"Knowing my scholarly father, it'll probably be something serious or very literary," Aram responded. "I know he loves the ODYSSEY and DON QUIXOTE. One time at dinner he and his college professor friend, Bob Carlson, were roaring as they read aloud letters that they had exchanged in Don Quixote's flowery chivalric style. Bob was visiting and wanted to cook an Italian dinner for us and our friends. He insisted that there be after-dinner entertainment in the form of stories. The entertainment was the letters he and Dad had composed in imitation of Don Quixote. It was so funny for these two old codgers to pretend they were in the middle ages restoring the age of chivalry and going off in search of adventures using this poetic, elegant language of medieval romance. Who knows? Maybe he'll read some of those letters. I hope he does. Everyone would burst with laughter," Mark surmised.

When the evening began, Michael announced that the title of the story was 'The Lucky Fool.' Already there was an irrepressible smile on his face as he began:

"Before I say another word, I want to testify that the following story is absolutely true, without the slightest bit of exaggeration or fabrication.

"When I was studying for a master's degree in English at

the University of Kansas in the 1960's, I wrote my thesis on the topic of luck in Henry Fielding's novel, JOSEPH ANDREWS. My adviser, Frank Nelick, recommended that I examine the proverbial sayings on the subject of fortune and fools as part of my research. Following his advice, I went to the library and read several collections of proverbs, looking under the headings of 'luck,' 'fortune,' 'fool,' and 'Providence.' Dr. Nelick knew that there was some essential, mysterious connection between fools and luck and directed my reading and thinking to explore this fascinating correlation."

"Please, Dad," interrupted Talene, "nothing too heavy or academic. Just tell a short, simple story. No one wants to hear about your dissertation on luck in Fielding's novels. No lectures, please. Just a funny or heartwarming human story and nothing too complicated. We're on vacation, not in college."

"Just listen, Talene," Michael defended himself. "The story is about to begin, and you're not even giving me a chance. This is not a lecture. As I was saying, I began reading these books of proverbs and found some gems like these:

> Throw a fool into a sewer and he will come up with a fish in his mouth.
> His net caught fish though he were asleep.
> Luck is a nickname for Providence.

Dr. Nelick was right: there is a rich lore and a traditional wisdom about luck accompanying the simple, the childlike, and the foolish. In proverbs and folklore the lucky ones are not the cunning, the sophisticated, or the worldly-wise but the innocent and the ingenuous who have no elaborate schemes for outwitting someone to gain a fortune. I quickly realized the distinction between the luck of the fool who lacks all guile and the shrewdness of the gambler who calculates to win.

"I was really enjoying this research and couldn't thank my advisor enough for introducing me to this wonderful subject. My thesis was becoming a labor of love. The fun of learning about luck made my graduate work seem more like play than work, more of a hobby than an academic requirement and exercise.

"At the time I was writing the thesis, I was also a teaching assistant at the university, responsible for two sections of sophomore composition. One day, after collecting an assignment of essays from my two classes, I was walking home after class on a Friday afternoon in April. As often happens, many of the papers were not stapled or bound with paper clips. On this windy spring day in Kansas a gust suddenly arose and swept some of the loose papers in my hand in all directions. I thought I had a firm grip even with the Kansas wind blowing, but I had underestimated Mother Nature. I rushed to collect all the loose pages I saw, moving in panic in all directions lest I lose a student essay and make a total fool of myself. I could see it now. I would stand up in class on Monday and make some feeble excuse like, 'I'm sorry, but as I was walking home from class, some of your papers blew away.' The whole campus would soon hear the story, and my notoriety would embarrass me before the entire English department.

"I felt confident that I had collected all the loose sheets as I had scattered in all directions with exceptional speed. I saw no more patches of white on the ground as I took my bearings and scanned the area. I anxiously waited until I could arrive home and check each essay for missing pages. What I had dreaded the most as I walked the rest of the way home had come true: several essays had missing pages, some as many as three or five handwritten sheets. As many as seven or eight students had at least one page that had disappeared. After this check of missing pages I realized that I would have to retrace my steps and search some more. That evening's walk produced not a hint of the lost pages.

"The following morning I made one final, desperate attempt to redeem myself. I paused near the spot where I had located many loose sheets when the wind first blew them from my hands. The area was near a parking lot that on this Saturday morning was completely vacant. As I paced in different directions looking for some evidence of white, I noticed a sewer. As a last resort I bent over and peered into the darkness below. Unbelievably, I did see some white-looking papers that I had assumed could only be litter that had fallen through the openings. I also noticed a stairwell that led to the bottom of the sewer where the white papers lay. I wondered if I could lift the sewer cover and discovered, to my utter astonishment, that it was loose and could easily be taken off. Descending into the underworld, I climbed downwards into the dark regions of mud and dirt, hoping that this ridiculous search was not in vain yet feeling skeptical the whole time.

"Wonder of wonders! The white, smudged papers at the bottom of the sewer were indeed the lost pages of student essays. 'What luck!' I thought to myself as I collected the missing, muddied sheets and congratulated myself on my great detective work and perseverance. My happiness had hardly begun when, amid the leaves and the papers, I spotted a $20 bill. 'Throw a fool into a river, and he will come up with a fish in his mouth.' 'Throw a fool into a sewer and he will come up with a $20 bill in his hand.' I was absolutely dumbfounded as I saw before my very eyes the perennial wisdom of the ages perfectly verified. I had proven my master's thesis without having written a single page—in a way that no faculty committee ever would have approved. I could hear God's divine laughter echoing throughout eternity.

"Once when I was teaching JOSEPH ANDREWS, one of Fielding's novels on luck, to my Restoration and Eighteenth Century Literature class, I told them this anecdote to impress upon them the concrete reality of luck as a universal experience. I wanted this episode of my luck in the sewer to make the novel come to life for them. When the members of the class turned in their next essays, attached to the last page of each paper was a xeroxed copy of a $20 bill. The luck of the old fool had returned. Assigning essays as an English teacher had suddenly become a lucrative business and teaching a picaresque adventure. These four outstanding students in my class perfectly understood and appreciated the mystery of luck more than all the other students I had taught for the past twenty-five years. They grasped the miraculous nature of God's sense of humor—the God who invented laughter, fun, and play and told us to be like little children.

"I repeat: four college students voluntarily paid their English professor four (xeroxed) $20 bills for assigning a paper on Fielding. No other foolish college professor can boast of such incredible luck and good fortune."

"Oh, I like that idea of luck as something that happens in fishing," remarked Peter. I can relate to that. It's called beginner's luck. I can remember the first time Dad took us fishing. After an hour of disappointment we were about to leave when my father asked where we thought the fish were hiding. 'Here,' I said, pointing to some random spot. Dad threw in the line and then asked in a serious tone if it was the exact spot I had in mind. After I said yes, we threw in the line, waited about a minute, then felt the tug, saw the bobber go down, and pulled out a good-sized sun fish. It was the first fish I ever caught. Pure luck! You're right, Uncle Michael, children, fools, and luck all go together."

"Something like that happened to me too," added Levon. "It happened right here on West Okoboji Lake the first time we came for a family vacation here. I caught a fish the first day and then nothing for the next eight days. I tried so hard each day, using a different technique or strategy each time. Once I tried to fish at the so-called perfect times for catching fish—early morning and early evening; another time I stayed in the same spot where I caught my first fish; other days I tried to use the types of lures other boys were using. I finally gave up trying. On the morning we were packing the car to leave, I asked if I could go to the dock one last time. That morning I caught fish in a matter of minutes without using any particular technique or special trick. Let's say 'His net caught fish though he were asleep.' "

"The passion for gambling has replaced the art of fishing as the modern equivalent of luck these days," Dickran noted. "State lotteries are big business, and people think of luck only as outsmarting the odds and winning big money. Luck is just blind accident, purely random chance. There's no grasp of the proverb in the story: 'Luck is another nickname for Providence.' Winning the stakes in places like Las Vegas is like playing a chess game and trying to outwit the opponent. That's how most people think of luck these days, if they even think of it at all. I was watching a baseball game on television, and the manager had to make a decision on whether or not to replace his pitcher. So what did he do? Did he follow his intuitions or instincts or use good judgment based on years of experience? No, he came out of the dugout with a computerized sheet that listed percentages. This pitcher had a better percentage of getting hitters out who were right-handed batters; that pitcher had a better percentage of getting batters out who were left-handed hitters. The exciting, daring game of baseball where you can steal bases, hit-and-run, and use squeeze plays is reduced to a safe game of statistical probability. Out go all thoughts about trusting in luck!"

"Let's remember that luck is often called Lady Luck or, in the ancient world, the goddess Fortuna," advised Michael. "The fact that luck is feminine says a lot. You don't outwit Lady Luck by cunning or conquer Fortune by brute force as Machiavelli advised in THE PRINCE. Luck has to be approached in a particular way. Lady Luck needs to be courted or wooed. The intentions have to be noble, good, and pure. Luck is not as blind or accidental as the lottery games suggest. There's some mysterious law operating that the proverbs and folktales illuminate by always mentioning fools, simpletons, and children as the lucky ones. Why lucky fools or lucky children or beginner's luck? They don't have elaborate designs or complicated schemes in the back of their brains. It's all very simple: they're just thinking of fun. There's no cunning or trickery involved, no deceit or involved strategies—just a purity of intention. What does the Lady demand? What is the test of love? That the man really love her, not just *say* he loves her. It's the sincerity that counts, not the words. What does the goddess demand? That she be honored and respected as a goddess, as someone above man—not someone who can be figured out or manipulated. That's right, Lady Luck and the Goddess Fortuna have feminine mystiques. They aren't just fickle or moody but act according to natural, albeit mysterious, laws that you can begin to understand a little if you really notice and observe."

"More or less like the romance in Tomas's story," commented Anna. "Aunt Siran was courted and wooed, and Uncle Tomas had to prove he was worthy. He had to wait for a second and third chance. He had to take the initiative, and he had to take a chance ('Should I ask her to dance? She might have a boyfriend or be engaged'). He had to stop calculating and computing ('It's too late; I'll be leaving soon; it's not worth it at this late date'). He had to be patient (Aren't fishermen supposed to be patient?) and not become discouraged because his first date was not a dazzling success. Why did Siran finally say yes? Because it was clear he deserved her and proved himself. Luck operates like that too. All you can do is invite luck and then let her decide. All a man can do is court a woman and let her make up her mind in deciding if he is the one for her. Strange laws, yes. But that's how these things work. There's always luck involved in meeting and marrying the right person—something that's not perfectly in your control and something that depends on your choices. Do you say yes or no to a priest who asks you to help him at his summer camp? Do you say yes or no to a chivalrous gentleman? Do you call again and give a woman a second chance when she had a bad cold on the first date? There is some rhyme and reason to this."

"It's not just baseball managers coming out of the dugout with computer sheets," Tomas interjected. "It's also deep-sea fishing boats locating schools of fish with their scopes, and it's computerized dating to find the right person, and it's opinion polls predicting the outcome of elections, and it's population controllers forecasting starvation and population explosions. It's the same mentality. Get rid of chance. Ignore luck. Do everything in a statistical, technological way. Eliminate the adventure, the romance, and the poetry of living. Deny the reality of a Divine Providence. That's what I see everywhere in modern culture. Now there's the possibility of cloning—the absolute form of control that leaves out Mother Nature, God, Lady Luck, the Goddess Fortuna—all the higher forces."

"Yes," Dickran added, "let's call it the Age of Control. Population control, birth control, language control, thought control. It's all the same thing. Don't let anything happen naturally or spontaneously. Fix nature and improve God. Make a Brave New World. So now they call a person 'a chair' and history 'herstory' and policeman a 'policeperson'. Oh, that really sounds elegant and poetic, doesn't it? Thought control—now that's something else. One of our children had to write an essay on 'women's issues' in TOM SAWYER. I'm not kidding. This classic boy's book had to be reduced to the politically correct theme of sexism—the bad light in which Aunt Polly and the Widow Douglas were portrayed. An essay topic was 'The treatment of women in TOM SAWYER.' Imagine every red-blooded boy reading that great adventure book and then having to write on that topic. What an agenda: 'Twain was a dead white male sexist.' "

"Nothing can have a life of its own or be true to its real nature," Siran commented. "Language can't grow and develop naturally like trees but has to be censored and neutered. Writers can't think independently and write from their minds, hearts, and souls but must have a politically correct agenda. Women can't be stay-at-home mothers and bear many children but must be feminists who find fulfillment in careers. Luck can't be surprising, unpredictable, fresh, or creative but must have its variations checked. To me the whole modern project amounts to the extermination of risk, chance, adventure, romance—all the things that have been mentioned—everything that the older idea of luck recognized about life and kept alive in our thoughts. The scientific control of the future so that all is predictable, safe, and tame, so that man is a god—the Controller—that to me is the whole theme of modernity. That's what the book BRAVE NEW WORLD is all about, and the character who fights this whole modern project protests in many of the ways we have been criticizing these trends. He says,

> But I don't want comfort. I want God. I want poetry,
> I want real danger, I want freedom, I want goodness.
> I want sin.

"And when man imagining that he can be godlike and determine or predict the future by technology, manipulation, propaganda, and population control has his way, then there is no longer any story—no tragedies, comedies, miracle plays, fairy tales, romances."

"I know, gone is all the wonder that is present in a person's story," commented Greg. "Think of the hand of Providence in

Grandpa's daring escape, the miracle of his survival, the luck of coming to America, a fairy tale of a story in which his life is totally transformed from the ugly to the beautiful. What an incredible journey—from a death march to the Syrian desert to the haven of America! From an Armenian marked for death to the father and grandfather of this family. To be human is to have a story that we can tell and retell to our children and grandchildren just as we are doing now. We all want to look back at our lives and say 'What an adventure' or 'How lucky I was' or 'I made the right decision'. Then there's meaning to your life, a plan. Man as god controlling the future means simply that we live comfortably and die painlessly and nothing else—a life of pills and drugs from ritalin to euthanasia. We hardly experience the heights of joy or the depths of sorrow—the things that speak most to our hearts. To live without hearing the stories about others or to live without having a story to tell is an empty life. No agony and no ecstasy. That to me is the greatest danger as we picture the nightmare of a future in man's technological control rather than in the hand of God's Divine Providence. Babies being cloned, pills to prevent birth, ritalin to keep you from being lively, video culture to keep you from thinking, and government and science to promise you heaven on earth and prevent you from thinking of death, heaven, hell, and the final judgment."

"How did we get from the tale of the lucky fool to the Age of Control and Huxley's BRAVE NEW WORLD?" asked Stepan as he recognized the lateness of the hour?

"Very easy, Uncle," replied Vahan. "It's life. It's all this human interaction. One thing leads to another which leads to another. It's all very natural and logical to go from luck to gambling to adventure to control. Real life is the opposite of the Age of Control. Everything reminds you of everything else. That's how people think and talk. It might seem random and wild like Lady Luck, but after a while you see a pattern, and it all makes sense—like our own stories. Thanks, Uncle Mike, I hope I can be a lucky fool like you. Let's see. I just have to fall asleep while fishing, go down into a sewer with my mouth wide open, and not try too hard, right? Oh, and I can't buy a lottery ticket, can I?"

"Not if you want to be a great storyteller and have one of these whopper tall tales to entertain your grandchildren with," quipped Michael.

CHAPTER TWELVE

Sunday Night: Meditations on the Beach

S tepan asked for volunteers for Friday evening's storytelling. His sister- in-law Anna answered his request. She explained that she didn't have a long story based on a single episode but a series of reflections based on things she had written in her diary from earlier family vacations. 'Can I just read them?' she asked, hoping she was not being too formal.

"By all means," Stepan reassured her. "It would be a pleasant variation, and it would be fun to know what a person is thinking when a person isn't thinking." So Anna began the evening's storytelling with a short preface:

"Whenever we go on vacation, I bring my stationery to write all those letters I have postponed for so long, and I bring my diary because I have insights that normally don't enter my mind. Being completely relaxed with no schedule of activities and enjoying leisurely days brings out the philosopher and writer in me. So here are a few reflections from my collection of meditations, all of them composed on the beach.

Meditation #1

"We don't want any children" or "we don't want another child" are thoughts that embody pure abstraction. "The child" is merely a disembodied idea, a lifeless concept. No one can love a generalization called "a child." It is the particular child that generates our love and awakens our parental instincts. The child that is born—the incarnate

reality—is not the same being that some parents imagined they did not desire.

God and Nature have created children as lovable beings. In their innocence, helplessness, and purity children evoke our love and pity. In their resemblance to us, their mothers and fathers, they are our prized belongings, our special, precious possession. Motherhood and fatherhood begin dramatically at the moment of birth when we realize that the being, nurture, education, and future of this unique person depend heavily on us. Instead of loving "the child," we fall in love with Talene, Peter, Mariam, and Levon—those dark-haired, smiling, affectionate, flesh-and-blood creatures who not only melt our hearts but also inspire us to have more children.

No one who has not been a parent can rightfully say, 'I don't want any children.' It is an empty statement without authority because the speaker does not know his subject.

"The child" is anonymous, an unknowable, vague conception. It is only with the incarnation of the child at the moment of birth that the full force of love begins.

Meditation # 2

"Daddy, cut the grass; daddy, cut the grass," my four-year-old son continuously repeats. He enjoys nothing more than watching his father start the lawnmower and trim the lawn as he 'helps' Daddy with his plastic lawnmower. Every day in the summer I hear the words, "Daddy, cut the grass!" It is a plea and a command at the same time. Our son's thoughts and imagination are preoccupied with this one activity. Even though I offer excuses and reasons that sound unintelligible to him, such as "the grass is not long enough" or "Daddy is tired" or "it's too hot," nothing daunts my son from insisting that the grass be cut every day.

Consequently, my husband finds himself mowing the lawn more frequently than ever before. He now feels obligated to do the chore at least once a week instead of every two or three weeks—his customary practice. The power of the right person making the request is amazing. If a wife, older children, relatives, or a landlord requested such frequent lawn care of my husband, it would have fallen on deaf ears. He would have felt imposed on and accused them of lawn-worship or vanity. "There are more important things to do," I can hear him saying. But how can he refuse a charming, delightful little boy this wonderful joy he experiences when Daddy cuts the lawn?

We must never underestimate the power and influence of the right person making a petition—a mother, a child, a saint. When the request comes from a sincere, pure heart, we cannot help but be touched and disposed to grant the wish. That is why the Church teaches us to pray to the Blessed Mother as our mediator, to seek the intercession of the saints, and to petition God in the name of Jesus. God cannot help but grant the prayers of those whom He loves and who love Him, any more than my husband could resist the plea of a son begging, "Daddy, cut the lawn."

Meditation #3

Our family is vacationing at Cape Cod in Massachusetts during a week of inclement weather. It is overcast and misty, hardly an ideal day for swimming. There is no special appeal or attraction on the part of the water enticing one to come and jump in.

Loving the water in all kinds of weather, I go for my usual swim. The water is just as warm, refreshing, and bracing as always, in spite of the lack of sunshine; but I cannot convince other members of the family to join me for an invigorating swim. The goodness of the water is not appreciated on this day because of the absence of beauty, the lack of sunshine depriving the water the splendor of light: there is no striking warmth, no lovely reflection on the water, no variegated color. Goodness requires beauty, attractiveness, appeal; beauty is, as the medieval schoolmen say, "the attractive aspect of the good," the splendor of the form, the outward aspect of inward worth. We must not only "be good," Henry Fielding writes in TOM JONES, but also "appear to be good." Good morals require courteous manners in order to be seen, known, and appreciated—one of the important themes in Jane Austen's PRIDE AND PREJUDICE.

At the same time a characteristic of wisdom, experience, and maturity is the ability to recognize the goodness without the beauty. One does not need glorious sunshine or 90 degree temperatures to en-

joy the ocean in the summer. The person in the act of doing goodness must take pains to be attractive and appealing: friendly, civil, clean, well groomed, appropriately dressed. The beautiful can and should reflect the good just as the body reveals the soul. The beauty of the ocean is an invitation to delight in the goodness of its waves. On the other hand, the person in the act of noticing or judging must transcend that which is immediately beautiful and grasp what is essential goodness. He cannot be limited only to the physical appearance or the first impression. A cloudy day or a plain-looking person should not make us prejudiced.

Meditation #4

Five children at the ocean, my three children and two nieces, are digging a trench on the sand of Craigville Beach, Hyannis, Massachusetts, on a hot August afternoon. They have been digging intensively now for over an hour, and the hole is as deep as their waists. "Isn't that enough?" one of the adults in our party shouts. "Aren't you kids going swimming on this beautiful sunny day?" I inquire as I look at the inviting waves and cool water beckoning swimmers on this ideal beach day.

The children keep digging and digging until the trench is now up to their chests. Another one of us parents yells, "That's enough! You're only going to knock it down and fill up the hole in a little while. Why are you killing yourself and wasting your time?" This practical question of course gets no response at all from the children. They all just keep digging. Two hours have now passed, and the hole is up to their chin. They jump in and proceed to bury themselves up to their chins with only the heads showing. Three of the children are interred, while two others fill the holes and perform the burial rites.

"You're getting sand in your hair," cries another mother. "Don't get sand in your mouth, face, and ears," she warns. But the children keep on reveling in the sand, lost in their own world and oblivious to all the practical, cautious objections of their dull, unspontaneous, grave parents. After they enjoy the sensation of being buried up to their chin, the children break loose from the sand and race along the beach. They jump and slide in the sand, caking themselves before they plunge

into the waves to clean and refresh themselves.

They have fun because they do something for its own sake, for the joy of it—not because it's practical, efficient, economical, or conventional. Parents tell them not to waste their time making ephemera with sand, but children experience eternity and timelessness as they lose themselves in play, tasting the sweetness of life. Parents schedule them and announce it's time to go in the water, as if the sole exclusive purpose of a day at the beach is to counteract the heat of the day. But children know that the ocean, like life, is a myriad of joys, not one pleasure. They enjoy the whole beach, not just the water alone; they savor the whole world that surrounds them there, not merely a single activity. So that's what St. Thomas Aquinas means when he says man is CAPAX UNIVERSI, capable of the whole universe.

As I look at the adult faces on the beach that day and notice the expressions of the adult relatives in our party, they are sleeping, idly reading, or sitting passively. There is hardly any conversation. We have run out of things to say and lack animation. In fact, the children digging in front of us have become our diversion, the focus of our attention. Whereas the adults on the beach limit their interest to one activity, the children before us dig, run, swim, and jump for joy. We exhaust our topics of conversation while the children bubble with laughter and animated talk. They not only revel in sand, sunshine, and water but also delight in the wonder of seashells, rocks, crabs, and minnows at the shore. They are in love with life and rejoice in the miracle of creation in all its beauty and goodness, reminding us of Robert Louis Stevenson's verse: "The world is so filled with a number of things,/ I think we should all be as happy as kings." And yet we unwitting adults limit and reduce their enjoyment with such inane remarks as "It's time to go in the water" or "Don't waste your time."

We murmur stupid objections and exaggerate trivia about sand getting in the hair, muddying their vision of the good and wonderful. Instead of being illuminated by the freshness of their insight and inspired by the vitality of their energy, we break the spell of their rapture. They are touching Being itself, and we interject, "Don't get dirty," dragging them from the pure realms of lyrical poetry to the flatness of drab prose.

When we are at the beach, the children are our teachers and lead us to the realm of pure heavenly play. They teach us to leave behind our cautious, reckoning, meddling, and middling minds that have forgotten to wonder and to enter the kingdom of God like a child.

"Well, Aunt Anna, I guess you are thinking about a lot when you're not thinking," Lucy said. "At least you weren't napping, skimming magazines, or daydreaming into space that day on the beach when this exciting drama was going on before your eyes. I'm amazed you were able to write a whole story out of this simple scene at the beach—so common and yet so extraordinary too. I really liked the meditation on 'Daddy, cut the lawn!' It's so true. How can you say no to children when they say, 'Will you read me a story?' or 'Will you play with me?' "

"Or how do you say no to your mother when she asks a big, special favor of you," agreed Aram. "Somehow you can't. When I was younger, I often wanted to go places without caring too much about my clothing. Oh, it's all right. It's not too dirty. It's not too casual. And my mother would say, 'Please, just do it for my sake. Your clothing is a reflection on me. What will people think of your mother if your clothes are soiled, wrinkled, or inappropriate?' So of course I would go back to my room and change my clothes to make my mother happy. I couldn't stand the thought of embarrassing her or hurting her feelings."

"I remember a college class in which a new instructor told us that for the final examination there would be both an oral exam, an in-class exam, and a paper due the same week," Mark interjected. "He justified all this work by saying, 'Each one of these assignments will help you prepare for the others.' I was skeptical at first, but there was a lot of sense behind the idea. I just accepted it and did the work. After the oral exam and the essay, the in-class part seemed very easy. I mention this because a group of students hated the assignment and complained among themselves constantly. They decided they would go as a group and petition the instructor to reconsider and change the nature of the exam. I knew their request would be denied, not because the teacher was unreasonable, but because of the spokesman for the group. It was the wrong person making the request. He had no credibility. Rob had missed more classes than anyone in that course, and his class participation was minimal. Let's face it: he was panicked. He knew an oral exam would expose his ignorance and lack of reading. But he was bold, glib, and argumentative when it served his purposes, and he convinced others to walk into the instructor's office with him believing the sheer number of students complaining would convince the young teacher to change his mind. If one of the best students in the class made the request, I'm sure the instructor would have listened and taken the complaint more seriously."

"I don't know how many of you may have read Augustine's CONFESSIONS in any of your classes," Michael added, "but Monica, Augustine's mother, is another great example of the right person making the request. After pleading with a priest to intercede with her son to change his pagan, degenerate way of life, the priest could only say to her, 'Woman, it is impossible that the son of such tears could possibly perish.' His prophecy was proven correct. It helps us understand why we say, 'Holy Mother of God, pray for us.' Look who is interceding for us! Remember that in the story of the lucky quarter, Uncle Tomas recited the Memorare: 'Remember, O most gracious Virgin Mary, that never was it known that anyone who fled to thy protection, implored thy help, or sought thy intercession was left unaided.' "

"Aunt Anna," commented Lucy again, "I've read PRIDE AND PREJUDICE and liked the meditation on the good needing to be beautiful and the beautiful hinting at the good. They should never be separated. If good people are careless about manners, dress, or speech, no one will discover or recognize their true character or go out of their way to know them better. Yes, it's true that polished manners, stylish clothing, and superficial friendliness can deceive—but not for long. All I know is that first impressions do count—at least as far as deciding whether or not you want to know this person more. We were talking about his point in class, and the instructor gave this example that I'll never forget. He said that he received a telephone call from an applicant for a position in English. The first thing she said was, 'I'm so and so. I am black, I am intelligent, and I am aggressive.' Now what kind of a first impression is that? She could have been the most wonderful person in the world, the most brilliant intellect, and a rare genius, but what a poor introduction! This is what the instructor said: 'Her first words implied that I was biased, that I could be easily intimidated, and that I was too stupid to determine if she was intelligent.' So, yes, I agree. You can't judge the water by the cloudiness of the day, but a beautiful, sunny day makes the water so much more inviting and enticing. Goodness needs to shine out and not be hidden. You have to try to be beautiful in manners, speech, and dress so that your goodness becomes revealed and visible. We don't light a lamp and put it under a bushel."

"The first meditation on the incarnate child," continued Anahid, "brought to mind someone I knew—actually a very good friend who often visited me at home for a cup of coffee after work. She had five grown children, the youngest daughter being about fifteen, when she became pregnant in her forties—a big surprise. She used to open her heart to me and confess that some members of her immediate family and other relatives advised against this birth. To her daughter it was an 'embarrassment.' Other members said 'it's your decision whether to keep the baby or abort it; we'll support you either way.' She would never abort a baby but was disappointed in the lack of enthusiasm and encouragement she received from her own flesh and blood. She gave birth to a boy that is now about the age of our Gregory. He'll be graduating from Princeton and is planning on going into law school or politics after graduation. Of course everyone fell in love with him after he was born. He was the darling of his mother, the pride of his father, the adorable little brother to his older siblings. Once again they forgot the difference between the so-called 'child' they couldn't possibly envision entering their life and this real baby—Jeremy—that brought all that laughter and joy into their home after all those years. Once the baby was born and in their hands, all their doubts disappeared."

"I couldn't help but relate to that last story of the children burying each other in the sand," remarked Melanie. "One of those adults on the beach could easily have been me before I had a family. I get carried away with neatness, cleanliness, order, and punctuality. I used to complain that Grandma Elise could have been a better house keeper, that she didn't have to have so much company at the house, that our home was not as picture-perfect when you walked in as other homes, that the boys had too many toys in their room, and too many friends over at the same time. Grandma would simply say, 'I can concentrate on cooking today or cleaning but not both'; today is a cooking day. When I grumbled about the house being in a state of chaos, all she would say is, 'Don't worry about the Monoply game on the dining room table or the chess game on the living room floor. They're having fun. It's *their* home too, not just mine or yours."

"When I moaned, 'Oh, no, we're not having company again!' she would say, 'That's what a home is for; it's not a mu-seum or a doctor's office, you know.' And then when I compared our kitchen with all the pots and pans on the stove and all the kitchen cleaning it required after meals to the immaculate kitchen at my friend's home, my mother's reply was classic: 'Do you know why the kitchen is spotless? They don't eat there. That's why. They eat out or order pizza almost every other night. Do you want to have chicken and pilaf here at home or go downtown and have hot dogs?' She was right. You have to live. You have to entertain friends and family with hospitality. You have to have fun. Your sense of order and neatness has to be human and real-istic. I learned that very quickly after the children were born. Who wants to stifle that irrepressible spirit—all that exuberance the chil-dren showed that day on the beach. Yes, I too learned from my chil-dren not to be so rigid and inflexible, thank God. And I was once rewarded with a beautiful compliment. A priest who had never vis-ited our home said to me just before he left, 'I could tell the moment I walked in the door that this was a happy home. How could I tell? I saw a piano, a game of Risk, and a chessboard.' And guess what a visiting nurse once told me: a home that is too immaculate, too spotless, and too neat is a dangerous sign of rigidity and inflexibil-ity—a place where children cannot be children."

"Well, it's that time again," Stepan intervened, "I'm see-ing some yawns, and my eyelids are also shutting. It was another full evening: stories from real life, good conversation, fun and laughter—a good time for everyone. Not too many evenings are left. I'm not sure who will tell tomorrow's story, but I know there are a few more we absolutely must hear. Let me see, who hasn't told a story yet? My dear sister, Anahid, you've been listening intently and absorbing all this wisdom and laughter, but now it's your turn to be the hostess as we become the guests. You are tomorrow night's *raconteur extraordinaire.*"

"Uncle, before Aunt Anahid continues with her story," interrupted Ara, "the cousins have a request. We have all grown up hearing proverbs. Could we devote a whole evening to hearing some of these classic Armenian proverbs—everybody's favorite ones. Whenever I hear them, they explain a situation perfectly, or they make me laugh. They are so down-to-earth, so practical. That's the kind of wisdom I love. It's easy to remember, and many are so unforgettably funny. They don't just have to be Armenian proverbs but favorite sayings or memorable quotations."

Uncle Stepan looked around the gathering and saw agreement and approval. 'Why not? Let's do it! A wonderful idea,' remarked Anahid. I'll just tell my story the following night. This will be a delightful surprise to see which proverbs and wise sayings are the favorite ones and then ask what special truth or wisdom the proverb offers. I love the idea. Great suggestion, Ara.'

"Good," Ara answered, "I'm glad everyone favors the plan. To tell the truth, this has become a kind of hobby. I've already begun to collect some of these sayings as I've heard them over the years, and this will add to my repertory."

The following night, then, some of the Bedrosians selected a favorite proverb, maxim, or quotation and weaved a moral or fable out of it.

CHAPTER THIRTEEN

MONDAY NIGHT: PROVERBIAL WISDOM

Ara was the master of ceremonies for the evening and asked Uncle Stepan to begin: "Uncle, please, you be first with some of those choice Armenian proverbs that you don't find in any other language. Let's see if we've heard them before."

"I'll begin with these two. I'll say them in Armenian as I remember them. First, *Chem oozer. kurbanees mecheh teer* (Translation: 'No, thank you, I don't want it; just put it in my pocket). Second, *tizhvar eh yergoohad tsmeroogeh shalges* (Translation: 'it's hard to carry two watermelons at the same time'). I remember our mother always telling us when we visited other homes, 'Always say no thank you the first time when offered something to eat or drink. If asked a second time, we could say 'yes.' How's that for delicacy and tact? What exquisite sensibility! You go out of your way not to inconvenience people, but you also do everything to please as well. Now that's manners. If the host insists that you partake of refreshments, good manners dictates that you be grateful and obliging and say yes. If the host repeats his invitation, it signals the sincerity of his hospitality and good will. The proverb simply means, 'Ask me a second time. I want to say yes, but modesty dictates I say no. But don't think that my 'no' really means no; it really means 'yes,' but I can't say 'yes' until you interpret my 'no' as a mere formality—an indirect way of saying yes. So as children we said no with our lips but yes with

132

our eyes. Now that is protocol and refined manners.

"To this day when young men and women from Armenia come as foreign exchange students, they are briefed on this matter of etiquette and specifically told that in America they will be asked but *once*. Say yes if you mean yes and no if you mean no, but don't say no when you mean yes: that's the advice they receive. Americans don't grasp the subtlety of old-world propriety or the finer shades of meaning in the customs of civility. Modesty, restraint, and good taste forbid blunt, direct honesty. You can't say what you're thinking: 'Yes, of course I want it. Give it to me now.' A good host repeats his offer several times, and then the guest is convinced that it is proper to say yes after a second or third invitation. The art of persuasion is involved here, and it's a highly developed one as you see.

"Why is that a favorite proverb? Because it's so comical and so human and especially charming. When I overheard my mother use it, I chuckled to realize that adults are just like children. They like treats and presents too, but they like them slipped into their pockets just as they are about to leave. It's charming because the proverb reminds us not to be too forward, too bold, too assertive, or too demanding. It also teaches us that real generosity is not just going through mere motions and formally accepting 'no' as the final answer. It teaches children self-control and proper behavior, the ability to be patient and to wait, and it encourages adults to make a strong effort. It's most unique and colorful.

"The second favorite proverb about trying to carry two watermelons at the same time reminds me of another classic proverb that Sancho Panza quotes for Don Quixote: 'An ass will carry his load but not a double load.' So many people defy the wisdom of this truth and try to do too much, acting as if they have no human limits. I talk to people at work, and they tell me 'I'm going to school at night.' These are people who work forty hours a week, take two of three courses a night in adult education classes because their employers are paying their tuition, and have families. I ask them when they study, and they tell me 'late into the night and on weekends.' I ask them when they enjoy their homes or families or relax, and they have no convincing answer, except that these rewards and pleasures will be postponed until they realize their goals. They're carrying two watermelons, and it's only a matter of time before one of them drops. Either their health suffers, or the children are neglected, or the spouse is ignored. That's not a human life.

"Younger college students also lack the common sense of the ass. Some of them work for us twenty to thirty hours a week. When I ask them why they work so many hours, the standard answer is that they are paying their way through college. 'So when do you study?' I ask. 'Late at night when I get back from work about 9:00 p.m' is the answer. 'So when do you sleep?' I ask. 'From 4:00 a.m.to 7:30 a.m.' is the answer. 'Are you awake and alert for your classes?' I ask. 'Sometimes, yes; sometimes, no' is what I hear. 'Is learning enjoyable, are you really learning anything, are you in any state of mind to be composed or relaxed enough to reflect and think deeply about your studies?' is my next logical question. 'Not really' is the honest answer I receive. So I then ask the hardest question: 'Do you see how you are defeating your whole purpose? You are working hard, making sacrifices, depriving yourself of sleep, exercise, and relaxation in order to acquire an education, but you have no time to enjoy learning, no leisure to contemplate what you have learned, and nothing to show for all those years except a certificate of graduation. Is that the value of an education?' The look on their face tells me that this is the first time anyone has explained things this way. Again, it's nonsense to carry two watermelons. You can't work that many hours and really study or truly learn.

"I also wish I could quote that proverb to many mothers who hold full-time jobs and then rush home to prepare dinner, do laundry, and manage a home. I wish the husbands who expect their wives to work could also show the common sense of Sancho Panza. How can a woman truly be a mother, a wife, and the heart of a family when she is also expected to be a breadwinner? It's doing too much. I have also been tempted in my work to take on new responsibilities, to work longer hours, and to increase my earnings. But at what price? If I don't have time in the day or evenings to talk to my wife, play with my children, read a book, enjoy exercise, and pray—then I know I am working too much and living an imbalanced, unnatural life. The proverb that warns about carrying two watermelons and Sancho's peasant wisdom always lead me back to reality and to sanity."

"Is it my turn next?" asked Melanie. "I wasn't sure which proverb or wise saying to select, but I have a good one. The women especially will appreciate this one. Grandma Elise always told her daughters, 'Be sure to marry a man who loves you a little bit more than you love him.' That sounds puzzling, doesn't it? Of course men and women are to love each other equally and totally and give themselves to each other; true love is always a mutual giving and receiving, loving and being loved back and forth and back and forth. That is the Christian teaching about love in marriage, and no one can question that. So what did Grandma mean? As a married woman of twenty-seven years, I think I understand. After years of marriage you will have your arguments and disagreements on all kinds of subjects; you will both discover that you have strong wills; you will both be certain that you are right and your spouse wrong. I forget who said it, but there is a saying that goes, as much as spouses love each other, they love their own will more. That means that one of you must submit, bend, or surrender, or the argument becomes interminable. That's not an easy thing to do. One of you wants to go on vacation to the mountains, the other to the ocean. One of you wants turkey for Thanksgiving, the other ham. One of you is ready for another child, the other unready. One of you wants to buy car A, the other car B. Of course these are matters you discuss in an open, honest, sincere way. But neither one of you convinces the other.

'You don't want these disagreements to continue and become unresolved because they then lead to conflicts and spoil the oneness that love always desires. Women realize they are harder to please than men and that little things matter to us more than to our husbands. If we want to change the curtains, just let us, and don't make up a hundred excuses not to go ahead. That's why it's necessary in a happy marriage for a man to submit to us in these smaller areas and not start a feud or insist on his own way. If we want to decorate the house a certain way, don't make a big deal out of it. We need a man who will go out of his way to avoid displeasing us. We need a man who will be patient with us, who will tolerate our moods, indulge some of our whims and preferences and not make these matters a major crisis. I think that's what my mother was telling us in her wise saying. In other words, marry a noble, chivalrous, large-hearted man—not someone petty with a fragile ego. A husband that loves his wife in this extra generous way will be a forgiving man. But she was revealing another secret to us in her proverb: a husband who submits to his wife in these small, everyday matters and surrenders his will to be pleasing redoubles a wife's love for her husband. Yes, we want someone who is larger than we are, someone who loves us a little more than we deserve. But we never forget the favor and become more endeared to our husbands because of this favor. Does that make sense? No, this does not mean that women always want to have their way and not be ruled by their husbands. It's just that in some of the areas of marriage a woman's judgment counts more than in others, and we want our husbands to know that and accommodate us. In other areas of marriage we will follow our husband's leadership."

"I guess it's my turn next," continued Tomas. This is a proverb I learned from a great coach: 'Sometimes when you do succeed, the chances are you weren't trying very hard in the first place.' Can you imagine that statement coming from a coach? Most coaches believe in a strong work ethic. Constant drills, frequent repetition, working on fundamentals every day, charts that indicate self-improvement by dint of will power and perseverance—that's the general philosophy of most coaches. So what did he mean by relating success to not trying too hard? As a great coach he knew the value of practice, discipline, and work. Every sensible coach and athlete knows that. But he also knew that there was such a thing as over-preparation and overwork. There's more to winning than hard work and will power and self-denial. Being relaxed, being spontaneous, and playing the sport for the fun of it rather than winning—these things count for much and play a surprising role in the outcome of athletic events. He used to use the example of Robin Hood with the bow and arrow. Robin was a great marksman, but when he shot his arrows he was never nervous, tense, or rigid. There was a looseness and fluidity—a natural gracefulness that came from loving the sport for its own sake and practicing for the sheer love of the game. Just because a team is drilled and trained through long hours of practice doesn't necessarily give them an advantage. I've seen surprising upsets in soccer by teams with average players who won a close match by their sheer exuberance in playing the sport—not because they had practiced some set plays and had them memorized.

"I knew someone in the physical education graduate school program studying for his Ph.D. He studied day and night, weekends and Sundays. He used to ask me, 'Where do you find time to exercise on a daily basis? Don't you have work to do, comprehensive exams to study for, and a thesis to write?' Of course I had as much work to do as he did, but I did the work with a clear mind and a relaxed body. I was more productive and efficient because I brought my best energy to my work, not my nervous stress. He never finished his degree, and I'm not surprised. He was too deadly serious, too much of a perfectionist. He kept changing his topic, and he revised and revised forever and forever. He was so busy being diligent and conscientious that he lost his perspective and grip on reality.

"The work-ethic often loses sight of the things that happen in our lives serendipitously, the gifts that come into our lives as godsends—like falling in love, meeting your wife, being surprised by good luck, or escaping from death. Just consider the stories we've been hearing all week. None of them are based on the moral that hard work alone wins the day. Think of children receiving fairy favors in the middle of the night—Santa Claus with his gifts, the tooth fairy with her magic, St. Nicholas throwing bags of gold into the homes of the poor. No one was trying too hard in those cases or undergoing Herculean labors. It isn't restless ambition or some frantic work schedule that is the secret of prosperity but the right balance of work and play, seriousness of purpose and lighthearted mirth, will power and relaxation, believing in yourself and trusting in God. That proverb gives you the right perspective on things, and it takes a wise coach to include that element in his game preparation."

"Aunt Melanie, it's your turn," Ara said. "Your favorite proverb."

"I must confess," Melanie began, "that I love that Armenian saying that Steve Mugar's mother taught him which someone mentioned a few nights ago: 'Do all the good you can, to all the people you can, everywhere you can, every time you can.' My favorite proverb is a slight variation of that one. It goes, 'Do good by stealth and blush to find it fame.' I'm not sure where I first read it, but it has always remained with me. It's a wonderful way of remembering that the good we do should not be for publicity, recognition, or reward. Good deeds should be done quietly, humbly, anonymously—that is, for the purest of reasons. I enjoy hearing about generous benefactors who choose to remain anonymous; their motives have to come from a pure heart. Remember in the story about Armenian friendship between Grandpa Nubar and his friend Grandpa Eli how everyone just assumed Eli worked for pay. No, he did good by stealth. Isn't that what the Christmas spirit is all about— giving children gifts and not revealing the true benefactor? The surprise birthday or anniversary party is another example of that same idea of hiding the goodness one intends. When I think of this virtue of concealing or forgetting one's good deeds, it's a beautiful testimony of the beauty of the human heart and the depths of love in human nature. It's the essence of Christian charity—not letting the right hand know what the left hand is doing, not keeping records of good deeds. It's not only giving without expecting to receive but also giving without being asked and giving without the hope of being acknowledged. Love can't be any purer than that."

"Uncle Mike, your're next," Ara said. "Please give us the final proverb of the evening and the reason you like it."

"It's my favorite proverb because it's true to life and helps me live wisely; it helps me understand how things work and how to make sensible decisions when I'm in doubt. You've heard it earlier, but I want to give you some variations on the theme, both from my life and from the books I teach. Remember how in Uncle Tomas's story he met Aunt Siran not once but twice and three times: he finally got the message. The proverb goes, 'When something is truly intended for you, it will come your way more than once.' I teach Jane Austen's novels in several courses. It's a main theme in two of my favorite books, PRIDE AND PREJUDICE and PERSUASION. The heroines in both of those novels both refuse a marriage offer from men they eventually marry. Even though they say no at first for various reasons—Elizabeth Bennet because of her prejudice and Darcy's bad manners and Ann Eliot because of family disapproval—the paths of these lovers cross again in the most accidental, uncontrived ways. Each time their paths cross, a new piece of information or a surprising revelation leads to a change of mind and heart. So they say no at first but gradually change their minds when they realize that their love is 'meant to be.' I've always been intrigued by that phrase and often wondered why some things are 'meant to be' even though we first resist them while other things are not 'meant to be' even though we wish them to happen.

Here's a personal example that also illustrates the truth of the proverb. I had received a sabbatical leave of absence for the spring semester of 1985. The academic dean had also circulated a memordum about a post-graduate seminar entitled 'Evil in Image, Experience, and Idea' for any faculty members who would have an interest. The seminar was funded by the Andrew W. Mellon Foundation and awarded a handsome $10,000 to each of the participants for a semester of study. I thought of applying and sent for the forms and papers; it was just a passing thought, a remote possibility. I wanted at least to entertain the idea of applying because the opportunity perfectly coincided with the semester in which I had a sabbatical leave. I thought about the idea for a few weeks and then dropped the idea. What were my chances of being selected, probably one in fifty, I speculated. These applications involve endless paper work, calling people for recommendations, essays to write. Is it worth it? The logistics of uprooting my children from school, looking for a family home to rent for just five months, and leaving our home vacant in the winter months when pipes can freeze also discouraged me from pursuing the matter.

"On the day of the application deadline, I received a telephone call from the director of the seminar inquiring about my decision: if I were still going to apply for the Mellon fellowship, late applications would be received. (Perhaps there were not enough applicants for all the available places in the seminar?) In short, I was assured that my chances for acceptance into the seminar were excellent if I completed the formal application forms and returned them as soon as possible. I began to realize that was 'meant to be.' How often does a professor on sabbatical receive a telephone call urging him to fill out some papers which will qualify him for a fellowship and receive a $10,000 stipend? At the time we had taken out a second mortgage on our home to pay for an addition on the house to accommodate our growing family. This gift seemed to fall from heaven. With the willingness and encouragement of your Aunt Anna, who loves travel and going to new places, I reconsidered my decision, changed my mind, applied for the grant, and learned that I was accepted for the seminar at the University of Kansas where I had completed my master's degree in 1965.

"All the logistical problems I imagined as obstacles and exaggerated as valid reasons for not going disappeared. A former graduate professor, Dr. Quinn, learning of my sabbatical semester at Kansas, volunteered with his wife Eva to look for homes to rent and quickly found one that was ideal for our needs as a family. If something is truly intended for you, the most complicated dilemmas resolve themselves quickly. Officially enrolled as an Andrew W. Mellon Fellowship participating in a seminar on the nature of evil, I discovered that the class met only a few times during the week. I had extra time on my hands to pursue other interests in a university setting. Coincidentally Dr. Quinn was teaching a class entitled 'Literature for Children' which immediately piqued my interest and motivated me to audit the course. What enchantment! Books like LITTLE WOMEN, LITTLE MEN, TOM BROWN'S SCHOOL DAYS, and THE WIND IN THE WILLOWS let me rediscover my childhood and enlarged my world. Here I was, an educator in his forties, falling in love with learning all over again in a children's literature class, thanks to the great inspired teaching of Dr. Quinn. It was 'meant to be' that I take this course and have another chance to learn the things which had escaped me in the past.

"So the chance to study children's literature was truly intended for me, and it came my way more than once. I began by auditing the class, then reading widely in the classics of children's literature, then creating my own course, and finally writing a book on the subject. When something is truly meant for you, you know it is God's will and that it comes from the wisdom of Divine Providence that orders all things for the good of all. Everyone in the family enjoyed that experience and all for different reasons. When something is 'meant to be,' it means that it is for the good of all concerned—for the common good of parents and children and for the benefit of young and old and for the future happiness as well as the present good."

"Before we finish for the night," remarked Ara, "is there anyone who wants to give us one more proverb or wise saying? His uncle Armen waved his hand and soon took the stage.

"This is my favorite quotation," Armen began, "and it comes from Chesterton. Chesterton wrote that many modern writers criticize the family for being a chaotic 'uncongenial' association of people, people who argue a lot and have many differences of opinion on a multitude of topics, but he defends the family for being a healthy and wholesome institution. He does not try to prove that it is a 'congenial' association but argues that 'the family is a good institution because it is *uncongenial.* Yes, I said uncongenial. The health and sanity of the family come from what Chesterton calls 'so many divergencies and varieties,' and he gives these hilarious, true-to-life examples. Younger brother George is not interested in older brother's religious doubts but in good restaurants. Uncle Henry finds his niece Sarah's desire to become a great actress unrealistic and impractical. Father is excitable and overreacts, Aunt Elizabeth does not make perfect logical sense. Younger brothers are wild and rowdy. The healthiness of the family for Chesterton is that it gives us a balanced view of ourselves and of the world: it keeps us from taking ourselves too seriously or overlooking our faults. You hear a lot of teasing. You don't get away with nonsense. No one is going to spoil you. It's rough and tumble and down-to- earth. No one can be a *prima donna* in a normal family or imagine he is the center of the world. Excitable fathers, unreasonable aunts, and mischievous brothers will not let you get away with it. You learn not to become a perfectionist or insist on your own way. What made me think of this saying is Saroyan's most uncongenial uncle who gave him the best piece of advice he ever heard: 'Have head examined.'

"My aunts and uncles," concluded Ara, "we won't forget these proverbs and sayings, I promise you—nor the stories that illustrate them. I'm glad I thought of the idea and asked you for your favorite, memorable ones. Thanks for the cornucopia that was overflowing. I know we could spend another whole night on proverbs, but we have a scheduled story for tomorrow night. I know Aunt Anahid is going to tell us a classic, right Auntie? In all honesty, though, those were good proverbs, but they can't compare with 'Throw a fool into sewer and he'll come up with a fish in his mouth.' Just kidding! At least we now know why the Bedrosians are all so normal and their family life life so healthy: we are all so uncongenial!!"

"Get ready for a classic," promised Anahid, "and also get ready for another trip to the lower world—not into a sewer but a dive into the bottom of a swimming pool."

CHAPTER FOURTEEN

Tuesday Night: A Dive into the Bottom of the Pool

On Tuesday night Anahid took her turn and began, "This is a remarkable story in our lives. I was driving home from Lucy's soccer practice when the light turned green at an intersection. I started to cross the highway, but a car that ignored a yellow light and then defied a red light was heading directly in our path. The driver was going so fast to beat the light that I knew our cars would collide. He barely swerved at the last minute to avoid direct contact, but he still hit the front end of our Plymouth Voyager van with considerable force, completely damaging our car and throwing us into shock. Miraculously neither Lucy nor I was hurt or scratched, but let me tell you all the events that preceded the accident.

"About ten years ago in early June we received a telephone call from close friends in Iowa who had recently visited France. On a spontaneous excursion not scheduled on the itinerary, the couple had meandered to the Chapel of the Miraculous Medal on the Rue de Bac in Paris where the body of St. Catherine Laboure lies incorrupt. Our friends spoke of the visit to the chapel as the highlight of their tour of Paris, and they mentioned purchasing for family members several of the Miraculous Medals at the gift shop.

"Our friends' experience had piqued my interest in this particular saint who, compared to the more famous saints I had known about like St. Francis of Assisi, was relatively unknown to me. In fact, I felt somewhat guilty and embarrassed at my ignorance and wanted to learn more about her life. A few days afterwards I was shopping at a religious bookstore where I noticed Mary Fabyan Windeatt's biography of the saint. Even though it was a simple children's version of St. Catherine's life, I felt compelled to read it and acquaint myself with all the facts of her life.

"Spellbound, I read the book in a few sittings. I admired the simple, modest, pious life of St. Catherine's parents, their generosity in raising a large family with small means, and their great love for the Catholic faith, which they transmitted in all its fullness to each of their children. When I read about the visitations of the Blessed Mother to Catherine when she was in her religious order, the Daughters of Charity, and then read of all the cures and miracles effected by the Miraculous Medal, I felt an overwhelming desire to acquire such a medal. The powerful image of the Mother of God with beams of light radiating from her outstretched hands to symbolize the abundant graces that Christ dispenses through His holy mother's Immaculate Heart stamped itself upon my memory as indelibly as it was impressed upon the medal. As I finished the book, the message of the Blessed Mother to St. Catherine echoed in my mind: As the Mother of us all, Mary desires all of her spiritual children to see the many graces that she will generously pour upon all of them. Yes, as she lamented to St. Catherine in one of her visitations, these abundant graces are not fully dispensed because they are seldom sought in prayer; many beams of light go unclaimed and never touch human lives.

"So naturally, thanks to a friend's visit to the chapel at the Rue du Bac and a children's biography of the saint, I wanted to own one of the Miraculous Medals. These events all seemed normal, probable occurrences—learning about something valuable and desiring to have a religious medal. However, a few weeks later when a good friend, Dorothy, was visiting our home, I noticed that she was wearing a chain around her neck with a holy medal. When I asked whether she was wearing the Miraculous Medal, Dorothy said yes and showed me first hand the very medal

I had read about in the biography. Of course I wanted to know where I could buy one and wear it myself. She told me it was a Catholic gift shop in Pennsylvania and promised she would give me the address. This sequence of events was now becoming most interesting. From France to Michigan to Virginia; from a phone conversation with friends 1,000 miles away to a book store a few miles from my home; and from pictures of the Miraculous Medal in a book to the real medal worn by a friend in my own home—the French saint and the Blessed Mother were sending me a message.

"Our ten-year-old daughter, Lucy, always attentive to her parents' conversations, had overheard my discussion with Dorothy and knew that I wanted to buy a Miraculous Medal. One hot July afternoon the children and I went swimming at a college pool. Lucy had been diving from the deepest end of the pool, looking for coins at the bottom. After one of her dives she came up with something in her hand and immediately turned to me: 'Mom, is this the medal you wanted?' It was indeed the Miraculous Medal, this time in the hand of my daughter. From a friend far away to a friend in the same town, from a chain around the neck of a visitor to our home into the hands of my own daughter, St. Catherine and the Blessed Mother were speaking to me in the language of love, although I did not yet fully understand their meaning. But I was certain that God wanted me to have this medal and to receive it from the hand of my daughter.

"About a week later at Mass the priest mentioned in his homily an American soldier in World War II hiding in a foxhole. Without warning, a Japanese fighter suddenly jumped into the foxhole and was about to take the American's life when he saw the Miraculous Medal around the neck of his enemy. No doubt a Catholic, the Japanese soldier interpreted the medal as a sign from God to spare the American's life. Of all the examples from history, literature, or the Bible that Father McLucas might have cited to illustrate his point, he happened to select this incident involving the Miraculous Medal (It is the first and last time I have ever heard a reference to the medal in any sermon all these years). All of a sudden St. Catherine Labouré, once an obscure saint about whom I knew virtually nothing, was quickly becoming a household word, a familiar name who was constantly present in my life. From early June to late July she was everywhere I went. What is going on? And yet I did not understand the meaning of all these things.

"The night before we left Virginia to return to Iowa, Dorothy, her husband Dan, and four of her children came to bid us good-bye and share a final meal together. As their family was about to leave that night, they presented all of us in the family with Miraculous Medals and chains. The Blessed Mother was touching the lives of each member of my family in a most tender, personal way. The graciousness of Mary had now encompassed the whole family. Remember that I had asked her for the address of the gift shop. Instead of merely providing me the name of the store, Dorothy's Christian heart generously bought not one but five medals and chains! Yes, as Pascal once said, 'Love does such things.' This last event seemed to be the logical conclusion of all the earlier episodes related to the medal—a gift to remind us of wonderful friends and fond memories in Virginia as we left to return to Iowa. Still there was something here I was not figuring out.

"Back in Iowa on a September morning, my daughter Lucy and I were returning home after her soccer practice. We were waiting at the intersection for the light to turn green when another car, traveling at a reckless speed, ignored his yellow and red lights and smashed into our car. Losing control of my car as it spun around and hit a light pole, I heard the terrifying sounds of shattering glass and metal clashing with metal. After the shock of this initial impact, I heard the shrill screams and uncontrollable sobs of my daughter. Fearing the worst, I finally stopped the car and asked her if she were injured. She assured me she was unhurt. I too was unharmed. The reckless driver received a severe cut on his head and came out of his car bleeding. Although both vehicles were totaled, Lucy and I escaped unscathed. When I returned to a normal state of mind after the trauma of the accident, I realized that I had experienced the miraculouness of the medal we were wearing. To be so close to the jaws of death and left unharmed could only to attributed to the Blessed Mother's intercession. I finally began to enter into the heart of the mystery.

Our friends from Iowa, Jane Ellen and Frank, who had begun this story with a phone call informing us of their visit to the Rue du Bac, heard about our accident and telephoned to express their gladness at our safety. I explained to Jane Ellen that I had been wearing the Miraculous Medal and recounted for her the entire sequence of events involving the medal's constant appearance in my life during the past few weeks. When I mentioned the detail about Lucy's finding the medal in the bottom of a swimming pool, she marveled at the remarkable coincidence of Lucy finding the medal to give to me to protect both our lives in that terrifying accident. As we heard in one of the other stories this past week, the more coincidental things seem, they less coincidental they really are.

"All these ordinary events—a telephone call, a trip to the bookstore, a child swimming at the pool, a priest giving his homily, friends coming to say good-bye—were leading us, step by step, to the Miraculous Medal, to St. Catherine Laboure, to the abundant graces of the Blessed Mother, to the Sacred Heart of Jesus. Now you know the end of the story. But, no, that's not the end. Another farewell gift that we received was a book, and in that book was a note from another well-wisher, Anita, who wrote in her letter the following:

> *Wishing you peace in the glory of Our Lord God almighty in everything you do.*
>
> *My memories of you and your commitment to truth will endure. Know that I will remember our many conversations on the subject. You and your husband and family are in my thoughts and prayers.*
>
> *Sincerely,*
> *Anita*

Included in the letter was a card I opened and read earlier. But now I re-read it with utter amazement. There it was again—

a picture of the Miraculous Medal on a membership card to *The Central Association of the Miraculous Medal* dated April 26, 1992. The card read as follows: 'Dickran and Anahid (Bedrosian) Derderian are members, and for one year will share in the benefits listed on the back.' This, at last, is the end of the story, I thought.

"When I passed on this additional information about these coincidences to Jane Ellen, who listened raptly to every facet of the story, she observed that it was exactly on April 26 that she and her husband Frank had visited the chapel at the Rue du Bac. She also noted that an article I had recommended to her from FIDELITY magazine, 'The Home as the Center of Civilization' (April, 1992) had on one of the same pages as the article a poem entitled 'Apparition at Paris' by David Lane—a poem about St. Catherine Laboure and the Miraculous Medal that I now reread with intense concentration. Here is a copy of the poem I brought:

> Guided by a cherubic child,
> Down once familiar halls;
> First a soft shimmering glow,
> Then a coruscating chapel
> Where hovers a Queen, stellar crowned,
> A pure prism of divine grace,
> With outstretched hands scattering rays
> Of miraculous iridescent love.
>
> Sublime prayer personified,
> Summation of all orations,
> Speaking celestial words
> To a humble cloistered daughter;
> And Catherine beholds the labor
> Of a Woman garbed with sunlight:
> The globe upheld in counter-revolution
> To correct its erratic orbit.

There can't possibly be any more, I reasoned. I now see the whole picture, the entire plan, this incredibly intricate design that could only come from a master artist's genius. But I proved wrong again. There was more. Shortly after I wrote to Anita about these events and thanked her for enrolling me in the Association of the Miraculous Medal, she wrote back with this astounding piece of information. I have the letter at home: 'My father escaped injury in a serious auto accident also. Even though his car was totaled . . . he was not injured. Your story caused him to recognize that the Blessed Mother's Miraculous Medal, which he wears faithfully, was instrumental in this favor.' "

"That was a classic, Aunt Anahid," commented Arpine. "What a tapestry of different people, events, and surprises all integrated into a beautiful design and most intricate pattern. It just reminds me of how united we are and how much our lives intertwine with the lives of others. All those different people in all those different places all doing different things, and yet the Miraculous Medal unites their hearts and lives. You begin to understand why Mary is known as the Mother of us all, caring for all her children and wanting them to be bound as one family of God."

"What was most striking to me," remarked Talene, "is the level of communication among the people in the story. It starts out with a telephone call, friends sharing their news. A woman learns about a saint and then reads to learn more about her life, a children's book serving as the organ of communication. A ten-year-old girl has her ears open and listens as her mother expresses a wish to have a Miraculous Medal; she does not forget what she has heard. It's not in one ear, out the other ear. A woman hears that her friend desires the address of a shop that sells the medals, and she answers the request herself with gifts of the medal for all the members of the family. She did not forget. There is the poem that is written to be read and to spread the story of the medal, and it is noticed. And there is the letter written to inform the family that they have been enrolled in the Association of the Miraculous Medal, and the letter is read and remembered. In that story notice how perfect the communication is. People really listen, really hear, really remember, and really communicate from one country to another and from one state to another. Such perfect understanding!

"To me it was a story of not only one family being specially protected by the Blessed Mother but also a story about a whole family of friends whose lives touched and blessed one another," added Vahan. The family calling from France about being at the Rue du Bac and the family giving the medals as a farewell present did not know each other personally, did they? But now they're related in a special way and by a real bond—by the love of a Blessed Mother and a Loving Father. So to me it's a story about a human family, a family of friends, and a family of God. And you see how the love is passed around and diffuses itself everywhere from person to person in the wildest of ways, bouncing from here to there in the most amazing movements. A great story!"

"Hearing you say that, Vahan, makes me think of Dante's great picture of Trinitarian love in the DIVINE COMEDY," remembered Michael. "It's a never-ending circle going back and forth from Father to Son to the Holy Spirit with the love breaking out in all directions and overflowing everywhere. I'll use this story as an example from real life the next time I teach the poem; it's an excellent analogy."

Another night rushed by. A whole vacation was almost past. Only one more night of a family reunion. The time accelerates when mirth and conviviality set the tone and create the atmosphere. No one was certain who the storyteller would be for the last evening or what kind of tale awaited them, but the two week vacation had brought everyone from the periphery of life to its center, to its source—to the rock-bottom realities of love, marriage, children, and families. The Bedrosian clan had impressed upon all its family members their indebtedness to a noble heritage, a rich patrimony, a Christian tradition, a precious legacy. They were not isolated individuals or random atoms in a void but members of an extended family and members of the body of Christ—a part of something greater than themselves, beneficiaries who had received much and who were now obligated to give as much as they had received.

CHAPTER FIFTEEN

WEdNESdAY AfTERNOON

The family reunion was coming to an end, the first of a kind. The cousins were pleasantly surprised. The stories were not *déjà vu* but old-vintage wine. The stories had body, color, taste, and substance—real food for thought—and they provided real pleasure and joy, not just passing sensations or ephemeral novelties. The cousins knew that their cup was full and overflowing, a banquet of emotional, intellectual, and spiritual provisions offered in the most bounteous hospitality. Their food for thought was not pablum, fast-food, junk food, or ordinary restaurant fare. It was home-cooked, seasoned, savoury nourishment from ancient, time-tested recipes passed down from generation to generation. Armenian food at its most delicious!

When people sit at a banquet table with different guests, the flow of information is not one-way, and the source of knowledge does not originate in one place. Men and women both have their kind of wisdom, and both young and old have their special insights. One thing was absolutely clear to the cousins. No television documentary film, no talk show host, no national newspaper or magazine, and no college course could equal this potpourri of a feast for the mind and soul. These stories were live knowledge, not dead information. All

these people, voices, experiences, and stories carried the resounding ring of truth, not half-truth, disinformation, or the
party line.The aunts and uncles did not invent truths, imagine fantasies, or speak in slogans or clichés. Everything they
thought they lived. These adults did not reduce life to sim-
plistic theories or twist reality into Procrustes' bed. They spoke
hard truths, never tickling the ears of youth by telling them
only what they wished to hear. The most impressive thing to
the cousins was that their elders opened their hearts in telling
their stories, and what beautiful hearts they revealed! As they
were relaxing on the beach on the final afternoon of their
vacation, the cousins commented on how much they learned
or discovered during this past week.

"The striking thing to me," Mark said, "is that Armenians really live. They are not afraid of living and living to the
fullest. They embrace all of life just as they cherish all their children. Remember that scene in Aunt Anna's meditation, the one
about the children on the beach digging in the sand, running by
the seashore, and plunging in the water? She said the children
taste all of life—wind, sand, and water. In hearing these stories, I
get the same impression. Our elders relish not only all the delicious flavors on the table but also the myriad of joys life brings
to them. They love their children and families; they appreciate
the beauty of love and romance; they cherish the goodness of
friendship; they love to joke, laugh, and entertain each other;
they love conversation, discussion, and stories. The reason this
strikes me is that so many people I meet at college or in my
summer jobs are really afraid of life and look for forms of escape. They are afraid to get married, afraid to have children, afraid
to spend money, afraid to take a chance, and afraid to leave things
in the hands of God's Providence. You can tell by all the hours of
television or videos they watch that they don't live rich, abundant lives."

"The Armenians of our parents' generation not only live
fully," remarked Mariam, "but they re-live and re-re-live their lives
as their stories and anecdotes illustrate. They love doing certain
things over and over again. They never tire of practicing hospital-

ity or tire of being mothers or fathers or learning and hearing from one another. They never tire of giving and loving: that is so obvious when we visit each other.

I have this sense that life for them is a beautiful piece of music or some great masterpiece of art which they want to hear and see again and again. Their love for life in their middle and old age is contagious. Unlike many of my jaded, blasé friends, they are more young at heart than half the people I know at college."

"As I've been hearing the stories each night," commented Ara, "I feel like I have traveled through all the ages of man: children racing along the beach, boys begging their father to play basketball outside, a man and woman falling in love, older birds with their proverbs of wisdom teaching young birds how to fly, Grandpa Eli taking the boys fishing in a taxi. Every one of these ages is beautiful in its own way, and there's always something to look forward to as we leave one age and enter the next. In the story of the outdoor basketball court I think of all the fun of being a child and playing a favorite game or sport day in and day out. In the story of the children in the art museum thinking it was a doctor's office, I think of all the comedy that goes with being a parent. In Uncle Tomas's story I think of the wonder of falling in love and meeting the ideal, perfect person to marry. In our parents' discussion about 'The Harvest of Life,' I think of a parent's joy in seeing his children mature into noble men and women. I think of being in my seventies and seeing my whole lifetime before me like Grandpa Nubar. What a feeling it must be to see your children's children and watch all their happiness and realize that you had something to do with all of this."

"What I've learned from this past week," reflected Lucy, "is that your life is a great adventure and odyssey. It's not just being born, ripening, reproducing, and dying. It's not just getting an education, finding a good job, and living a comfortable life of ease. It's a novel or drama in which miracles are always possible—sorrow turning into joy, good coming out of evil, light coming out of darkness. Aunt Siran lying there in the hospital and seeing Uncle Tomas bring her the quarter she was praying for as a sign from God. We really never know what is going to happen next. Who would have ever guessed that Grandpa Nubar would escape from the desert and raise a family in America? Who would have ever guessed that Uncle Tomas's decision not to go to Europe would lead to his meeting his lady love? Who could have imagined the power of the Miraculous Medal in an automobile accident?"

"As I've been listening to these stories," Arpine remarked, "I keep noticing the theme of dreams and wishes coming true: a child wanting a red wagon, boys wishing to have their own outdoor basketball court or go fishing, a pregnant mother suffering with toxemia wishing her husband would bring her the sign she prayed for, a woman praying to meet a man who would satisfy her qualifications for an ideal husband. All these dreams and wishes come true. I've always wondered why some wishes come true and others don't, and I think I learned why in a children's literature course I took last year. The stories of wishes coming true I've heard on this vacation verify everything I learned about this topic in my class."

"You have to tell us, Arpine," insisted Tamar.

"We were discussing the fairy tale 'Aschenputtel' (Cinderella) in the Grimm folktale version," Arpine continued, "and the professor asked us to distinguish between a wish, a fantasy, and a whim. It became clear from our discussions that true desires originate in the heart and in the depths of the soul. They are constant and do not die out or disappear. Because they are so powerful, they inspire effort, determination, perseverance, sacrifice, and prayer. A person does everything in his power to make a dream come true, taking risks, embracing opportunities, and overcoming obstacles as Aschenputtel does. When a true wish is granted, a deep, lasting sense of happiness follows—a feeling of living happily ever after—rather than a restless search for more things or novelties.

"A true wish differs from King Midas's fantasy about the golden touch motivated by greed and the fisherman's wife's fantasy about being king, pope, and God, a daydream motivated by envy. A true wish comes from a pure heart, from a natural human desire for happiness, and it differs from a whim—a desire for novelty, change for the sake of change, a wish that is influenced by the suggestions of outsiders. The thought that kept crossing my mind as I thought about all the wishes that came true in the stories we've been hearing is this: God does not place true wishes in our hearts unless He plans to satisfy them in some mysterious way and at some ripe moment. I even read somewhere that Mother Teresa said this very same thing."

"Do you remember how Uncle Stepan one night asked us to compare the old and the new, to contrast the learning in these stories and in our conversations to the education we receive in our schools and colleges? I think we've been doing that this afternoon," remarked Harry. "Wisdom and education are two entirely different things. Let's tell him tonight all the things we've been saying here this afternoon. By the way, I wonder what the final tale will be, and who will tell it."

CHAPTER SIXTEEN

Wednesday Night: Father Arakelian's Sermon

As everyone gathered for one last time before the end of the Bedrosian reunion, Stepan began the storytelling time tonight with a prayer:

"Dear Lord, we praise you for the glorious beauty of this summer season and the heartwarming joys of a family reunion. We rejoice in all of your creation: the refreshing water, the radiant sunshine, and the rejuvenating wind that have renewed our spirits. We give thanks for our parents and children as we marvel at your great plan and artistic design in each of our lives. We remember that you did not create us to be alone but to be members of a family: to marry and to be fruitful, to give and to receive, to love and to be loved, to inherit and to bequeath. We lift up our hearts in the knowledge that we are made to be one in the bond of family, in the union of marriage, and in communion with You, to love and to be loved, to inherit and to bequeath, and to love and to be loved. Through the power of the Holy Spirit may we continue to be blessed in our marriages and in our families so that we may always be a source of grace—a special gift or blessing—to one another: husbands to wives and wives to husbands , parents to children and children to parents, brothers and sisters to one another, and each family to other families."

"And now to conclude, not with a story but with a sermon. Michael tells me that Chaucer concluded THE CANTERBURY TALES with a sermon on the seven deadly sins, so there's precedent for this last of the BEDROSIAN TALES. On the last Sunday of the camp season, I came to pick up our children at St. Gregory's Armenian Camp and also go to Mass at the chapel there. At this Mass Father Arakelian delivered a sermon I will never forget. It moved all the parents present as much as it spoke to all the children. Since it was the final day of the last week of camp, Father Arakelian naturally noticed the sadness of the children saying good-bye to their best friends. For the past several weeks many of these children who were once strangers to each other had discovered the bonds of true friendship and acted as if they were eternal friends. The campers were exchanging telephone numbers and addresses, promising to correspond with one another and making plans to return the following year. It was a poignant farewell scene, reminiscent of saying good-bye at graduation or farewell to old friends after retiring or moving away. Seeing the tears on the faces of many of the girls and the sad expressions in the eyes of the boys, Father Arakelian spoke his children's homily in words like these:

'Many of you are sad to see camp end and see the summer come to a close.

'Many of you are sad to say good-bye to friends who live far away from you, friends you may not see again until maybe next summer. Remember, though, that when one beautiful thing ends, another beautiful thing begins. That is God's plan for both children and parents. Yes, summer is ending, and the camp season is finished. But as this beautiful time ends, another beautiful time begins as you return to your good homes and loving families.

'Your parents did the same thing when they married. They said good-bye to their mother and father, and it was a time for tears. A beautiful time in their life had ended as your mothers and fathers left their familiar homes and dear parents. But as this beautiful time ended, another beautiful time began. Your parents became husband and wife and began their own home and started their own family. A new joy replaced an old joy. Your parents had to say a good-bye for you to be born and to know the happiness of being a mother and father. You too have to say good-bye so the next beautiful chapter in your life can begin.

Remember that you never ever really say good-bye forever. You can see each other next summer. You can visit each other if you do not live too far away. You can write or call one another, and you can always remember one another and pray for each other. Your mother and father said good-bye to their parents for just a little while until they visited each other again. You too are saying farewell just for a season. Love never ends, goodness never goes away, and beautiful things keep coming into our lives. So, dear children, do not be sad. When one beautiful thing ends, another beautiful thing begins.'

"It was one of the most eloquent, touching sermons I have ever heard, and it was addressed to children. I remember it almost verbatim, and it was twenty-five years ago. The parents at Mass that morning were in silent awe. Afterwards I recall one woman turning to me with tears in her eyes, commenting, 'Wasn't that one of the most beautiful sermons you've ever heard?'

"That story and sermon are not only appropriate for the end of camp but also perfect for the end of our family reunion. We began with Grandpa Nubar's life. He and Grandma Elise are no longer with us; their beautiful lives have ended. But another beautiful thing has begun, the lives of their grandchildren. The happiness of romance and falling in love and being engaged has ended for your parents, uncles, and aunts. But another beautiful thing has begun—seeing the happiness of their children and anticipating their engagements and weddings. Yes, there is a sadness in saying good-bye to the fun of playing basketball, going fishing, and being at Fenway Park to see Ted Williams, but there is the beautiful experience of fatherhood to replace it. Yes, there is a great sadness in being a widower like me and knowing my beautiful marriage has ended, but some day—God willing—another beautiful thing will begin. I will be reunited with my wife, my mother and father, and all my loved ones in the life to come when every tear will be wiped away and when we will never be sad again or have to say good-bye.

"Remember Grandpa Nubar's sadness in being torn from his mother never to see her again. Remember the sadness he expressed in his greatest longing—*hokees goodum haires yev maires desnum* (I would give my heart and soul to see my father and mother). God does not give us such deep longings and profound desires if he has no intention of answering them. God puts these desires for beautiful things in our hearts because He wants our wishes and dreams to come true both here and now and forever and forever."

When Uncle Stepan finished his story and sermon, it was as unforgettable to his nieces and nephews as Father Arakelian's homily was to the parents at St. Gregory's Armenian camp.